Approved by the Kundalini Research Institute

Waves of Healing

Listening to the Voice of Your Soul

Siri Atma S. Khalsa, M.D.
Based on *The Teachings of Yogi Bhajan*™

YOGIC REALITY
pure healing

CREDITS

Project Editor & Production Manager:
Nam Kaur Khalsa
Book Designer & Cover Art: Rai Singh Khalsa,
Acuario Pro. Ltda.
Photographer: Gary Steinborn, Venice Clay
Yoga Model: Annmarie Solo
Meditation Model: Dr. Siri Atma Singh Khalsa
Editorial Consultant: Siri Neel Kaur Khalsa, KRI
Spiral Wave Artist: Cortney Bodnar, Light Artist Photography

Publisher:
Yogic Reality Inc.

$39.99
ISBN-10:   0-615-29555-X
ISBN-13: 978-0-615-29555-8
53999>

There is a wisdom that is the harmony of your being. It resounds the music of your spirit and spreads like waves to everyone in your vicinity.

— YOGI BHAJAN

FOREWORD

During one of his daily medical check-ins, our Teacher, Yogi Bhajan, recommended that my husband write a book called *Waves of Healing*. A year after Yogiji's passing, I reminded my husband about the book and he said, "I'm not a writer." I replied, "Maybe not, but you are a teacher." I suggested he create an outline of the chapters and *teach* them, as he is never at a loss for words when teaching! So for the next two years as we traveled to yoga centers, solstices and international yoga festivals in Chile and France, I recorded his workshops.

My work for the Kundalini Research Institute (KRI) involved working closely with Yogi Bhajan. I was aware that he had reviewed and approved the write-ups of some of the earliest yoga classes he had taught in Los Angeles before they were videotaped. And fortunately these previously unpublished kriyas fit perfectly with Dr. Siri Atma's *'Ten Body Healing'* concept. *Waves of Healing* explains this, and much more.

Nam Kaur Khalsa

INTRODUCTION

We live in an information age; in a matter of hours, we can find an expert on any topic we seek and meet them online. In such a world, we cannot spend our lives only sharing knowledge we have learned from others. What we must share is the knowledge we have acquired through experience, and the truth innate within us.

In *Waves of Healing* I will share the understanding of yoga, health and healing which I gained over 30 years with my spiritual teacher Yogi Bhajan and working with my patients and yoga students. Very little of this wisdom was communicated verbally; it came from spiritual experiences so profound as to win over the doubt and disbelief of my atheistic upbringing and western medical training.

Siri Atma Singh Khalsa, M.D

TABLE OF CONTENTS

Chapter 1

THE TEN HUMAN BODIES

You may believe you only have one body to care for, but in reality, each of us has ten bodies.

— DR. SIRI ATMA

Chapter 1
THE TEN HUMAN BODIES

You may believe you only have one body to care for, but in reality, each of us has ten bodies.

I realize this may sound absurd, as most of these bodies are not visible to the human eye. The thoughts created by these bodies are not visible either but our lives revolve around them. In fact it is through the thoughts generated by these bodies that we perceive the nine bodies best. The practice of Kundalini Yoga gives us the subtlety to sense and balance our ten bodies.

> *If you understand that you are ten bodies, and you are aware of those ten bodies, and you keep them in balance, then the whole universe will be in balance with you.*
>
> **– Yogi Bhajan**

These are the ten human bodies referred to in the science of Kundalini Yoga as taught by Yogi Bhajan:

I THE SOUL ~ The soul is the timeless body that contains our being, consciousness and personality. The other nine bodies were given to serve the soul, the real subject of life.

II THE NEGATIVE MIND ~ The negative mind calculates risk; it was given as a protection so we may know how things are going to hurt us.

III THE POSITIVE MIND ~ The positive mind calculates benefit; it was given so we can know how things can work to our advantage.

IV THE NEUTRAL MIND ~ The neutral mind evaluates risk and benefit; it was given so we can recognize how things relate to time and space.

V THE PHYSICAL BODY ~ The physical body has the capacity to correlate our activities so we can come through; it was given to share feelings and emotions.

VI THE ARCLINE ~ The arcline is the halo around us that guides and controls our aura; it was given as a shield, a protection.

VII THE AURA ~ The aura protects us from other people's negativity, and gives us sensitivity to our environment; it was given so we can reflect ourselves.

VIII THE PRANIC BODY ~ The pranic body gives life to the physical body and is connected to it through the breath; it was given so we can live.

IX THE SUBTLE BODY ~ The subtle body gives the capacity to learn quickly; it was given so we can understand the nuances of life.

X THE RADIANT BODY ~ The radiant body's magnetic attraction gives us courage; it was given so we can influence and prosper.[1]

The practice of Kundalini Yoga strengthens all ten bodies procuring permanent changes in our perceptual reality. Our newfound awareness allows us to focus on the voice of our soul, which guides us in fulfilling the purpose of our life.

When we keep the ten bodies balanced, we create waves of consciousness that lead to authentic healing. We will explore the ten human bodies further, but let me start from the beginning, so you can learn about them the way I did.

Chapter 2

MY STORY

I love to learn.

— DR. SIRI ATMA

Chapter 2
MY STORY

I love to learn.

As a young boy I did well in school and was placed in a gifted program. This served me academically; however, when I left home for college, I was totally unprepared for what I would encounter. The year was 1976. While I was younger than the Timothy Leary crowd, I felt a kinship with their search for peace and truth. I asked myself what were then considered the 'BIG' questions: *Who am I? What is the meaning of life? What am I going to become? How will I contribute to the great society?*

When I was fourteen, my father told me that no matter how good I would become at anything, I would always find someone better than I was. This statement rang true, but there was also a falsehood to it, and by the age of sixteen, I had figured it out:

The one thing I could be better at than anyone else was being me.

This was a frightening concept. I was terrified to express myself for fear of social rejection. To solve this issue I started reading spiritual texts, believing that by reading the works of the great masters I would discover myself.

One day I realized I was not reading to discover the truth; I was looking for someone to validate *my* truth. It occurred to me that unless there was someone else exactly like me, I could spend my entire life searching for validation instead of discovering my truth through self-expression. I decided that if I took my path, I would be more likely to encounter like-minded souls.

Destiny guided me to Yogi Bhajan, a great man of God. However, I wasn't convinced of his wisdom prior to meeting him. When I went to hear him speak for the first time in 1979, I devised a plan to test him out. I didn't know enough to check out his spiritual knowledge, but I did know that with the force of my projection I could push most people off their center. My plan was to take him by surprise. If he failed – game over – I would move on.

The conference hall was crowded with yoga students bustling around Yogi Bhajan. I could see him from across the room; his magnetic presence was unmistakable. I lost no time. Focusing my eyes on him with all the psychic power I could muster, I silently screamed, "So you're the great Yogi Schmogi everyone's talking about. Prove to me you're a Yogi!"

In a steady and courteous manner, he turned his head and locked his eyes with mine. He didn't speak aloud, but I can still hear the words he silently issued: "If I am a Yogi, that is my blessing. If I am not a Yogi, that is my problem. Proof that I am a Yogi is that I don't react." And with that, he turned away and continued talking to the young man at his side.

In that moment, my life changed forever. I recognized Yogi Bhajan as the voice which had been giving me inner guidance. His psychic ability was impressive, but even more so was the grace with which he had deftly avoided my confrontation. On the spot, I gave him ten years of my life; it never came up for re-negotiation.

Prior to meeting Yogi Bhajan my mind was full of images of living austerely and meditating in a distant Himalayan cave. The moment I met him, I knew with a strange certainty I would instead complete my college education. I was so excited about finding a teacher that I didn't pay much attention to that part of me that 'knew.' When I began studying with Yogi Bhajan, my ego was attracted to spiritual power. The social status of being a saint or great healer was attractive to my ego, while the good deeds performed by being saintly was attractive to my soul. Thus, when I started the spiritual path my ego and soul were in alignment. Both wanted the same thing for different reasons.

For years before attending medical school, I did specific meditations to gain the ability to heal with my mind. My ego desired to be the greatest healer of all time, or at the very least, capable of performing miracles. In those days I did not consider universal laws as beautiful. I thought proof of God's existence would be to see a universal law bent or broken just for me!

In the Intensive Care and Cardiac Care Units, patients are within hours of death. While practicing there, I discovered I could do everything by the book, get everything right, and still the patent might die. I eventually learned that my job was to do my very best, but that the ultimate outcome was not under my control.

Chapter 3

BEING TRUE TO YOURSELF

The 'self' is a combination of five of our ten human bodies.

– Dr. Siri Atma

Chapter 3
BEING TRUE TO YOURSELF

The 'self' is a combination of five of our ten human bodies.

When we think of what comprises our self – we often think of the commonly quoted phrase *'body, mind and soul.'* More specifically, the self is a combination of five of our human bodies: the physical body, the three minds (negative, positive and neutral) and the soul.

When I was sixteen and about to shave for the first time, I looked in the mirror and asked myself, *Who do you want to look like?* The question was absurd. Here I was reading *Siddhartha* for the seventh time, trying to discover who I was, and already I was contemplating copying someone else's identity! I made a commitment to myself that I would never shave or cut my hair until I knew who I was, figuring that at least when I looked in the mirror I would see the physical manifestation of my true self.

Every human being is unique and will live a unique life. The thoughts that create our unique truth are the most valuable things we have. Your truth isn't found in a book or in someone else in exactly the same way. You do not learn your truth from someone else, or from somewhere else. It is not something you learn in school or hear on television. When I meet you, I want to know what only *you* know. Your inherent truth is the one thing I cannot learn from anyone but you.

You have to find your 'you' and experience it; that is the total purpose of life.

– YOGI BHAJAN

You can become aware of who you truly are by studying situations in which people offend you. Why? When people hurt you, bump into you, or step on your toes, it is because you have a sensitivity they don't have. You know the dance; they are fumbling through this aspect of life. Often when you are hurt by others, it's because they don't have the insight you have. When people offend you, it reveals the subtlety or innate truth you have which they lack. Since the subtle body and soul are linked, that subtlety is your awareness of your soul. The subtlety of life is revealed when the voice of your soul speaks and your truth is manifested. This is how I describe *'listening to the voice of your soul.'*

When you explore values deep inside, values you are passionate about, you are uncovering your own truth. When you live to these values, you become your own best friend. When you ignore your truth or subjugate yourself to someone else's truth, you betray yourself. Believe it or not, you will develop the same feelings towards yourself that you would have towards anyone who betrays you.

As a physician, I've found that in the course of treating illness, it often comes down to the core issue of being oneself. We do not have to do anything to be ourselves; all we have to do is stop trying to be someone else. The secret is, don't discover yourself, don't transform yourself and don't recreate yourself. *Nurture yourself and see what you become.*

Many of my patients tell me that being authentic is the most daunting task they have ever attempted. Creating environments that nurture your inner nature provides security in which you can begin to heal. For me, planting trees is extremely nurturing. Trees live for hundreds of years, transforming their surroundings with shade, peace and beauty. Seeing them grow inspires and nurtures me at a deep level.

Have you ever seen a magnificent tree alone on a ridge, with a fully expanded crown? Even if you've never seen this variety of tree, you can tell it is expressing its complete form. You may not know the hardships that buffeted this unprotected tree but you can appreciate its strength. You can admire its grace and beauty and gain courage to express your authentic self.

The authentic self isn't created as much as it is *nurtured* into existence. Ask yourself, *What has kept me from being me? What environment do I need to be authentic? How can I create this environment for myself?* Create a safe and nurturing environment in which you can unfold. Trust me; no one else can be you better than you can.

I see people spending a tremendous amount of time and energy trying to change who they are, instead of learning to love and accept their strengths and weaknesses. This is a life of polarity, there's no doubt about it. Your greatest strengths can come out of your weaknesses. If you just focus on eliminating weakness you may miss the lotus flower growing out of the mud.

I've always been rather naïve, and for many years I contemplated changing this aspect of myself. One day I realized that if I was successful in eliminating my naiveté, I would lose my innocence, which is the source of my enthusiasm and joy.

> *You have to know your strengths and weaknesses. Between your strengths and weaknesses is you.*
> – YOGI BHAJAN

We are created by God, and as such, we are infinite. How can we have an experience of that totality? *Through our identity.* The only way to experience the totality of God is through your identity. When you know who you are, and who your Creator is, you see yourself and the Creator as one. That is the experience of the Infinite.

When the psycho-electromagnetic field of a finite subject, the being in a human being, is capable of tuning into the vibration of the universal electromagnetic field, that man is in a state of consciousness where the difference between the finite and Infinite become one. It is called a state of yogic consciousness.

– YOGI BHAJAN

Chapter 4

AUTHENTIC HEALING

*If we are very sick we have to change our
electromagnetic frequency.*

– YOGI BHAJAN

Chapter 4
AUTHENTIC HEALING

If we are very sick we have to change our electromagnetic frequency.

– YOGI BHAJAN

This concept took me years to understand. When I became an Intern I thought, *Now I will practice medicine, but secretly I can do psychic healing.* After three weeks I became very ill. I watched my illness develop because I wanted to be the *'Doer.'*

 The illness stopped my world and brought me back to reality. It made me realize that my patients were probably also going through important life lessons. It was not my job to take away their lessons, but to help them understand so they might learn through less painful means.

I had begun my entire pursuit of spirituality, medicine and healing from a mistaken premise. I thought the more I knew the more control I could have and the more pain I could alleviate. Now I found that even as a doctor with 13 years of training, I was unable to heal people when there was no cure, or even treatment, for their illness. All I had to offer these patients was pain management, comfort measures, love and caring.

Eventually I learned that in every healing situation there are three things I need to know: *What is my responsibility; what is the patient's responsibility; and what is God's responsibility.* I found it was less important to know everything and more important *to know what to do*. I began to count more on listening to my soul to ascertain not just the facts of the situation, but the right action to take. I concluded that: *Experience beats intuition in every case except when my intuition tells me, 'This case is different; your experience won't help.'*

Given the gravity of the life and death situations I was dealing with, I thought it wise to check with other doctors about my newfound philosophy. In this way I established *'due diligence'* within the framework of my professional code.

Learning the boundaries of healing did not help me accept them. Still bothered by the fact that I wasn't able to heal everyone, I sought advice from a therapist. I enjoyed our first session and went home feeling much better. As I was falling asleep that night, I could feel the healing power of her kind thoughts and genuine concern for me. This validated my belief that being truly cared for was paramount to the healing process.

After residency, I moved to a small town in northern New Mexico, and began a private practice. Working in a clinical setting for over a decade, I learned to see illness arising from the thoughts, habits and actions of my patients. I realized that properly managed with preventative medicine, very few of them would ever need to use the Emergency Room again, and fewer still would need hospitalization.

Once a patient's condition is stabilized, I discuss what led to their disease and work with them on improving their habits to re-engineer their lives. As you might expect, this is quite a challenge, both for the patient and myself.

Changing attitudes, beliefs and habits that lie in the unconscious mind requires more than patient education, though this is a good first step. Facing a serious illness often forces patients to evaluate the way they are living for the first time. At this stage they can accept that spiritual growth and lifestyle changes are essential in order to heal.

Many people seek a spiritual path because they are experiencing what I call *'spiritual illness.'* Who they have become is different from their identity as created by God. When patients are ready I explain my philosophy about spiritual illness and ask if they feel they have been true to themselves:

The distance between who you are supposed to be and who you've become is the amount of disease, suffering, and depression you manifest in your life to compel you to close this gap.

Who is experiencing this life? The soul. Your soul comes to this life with ideas, beliefs, emotions, and personality. The soul records your actions and your beliefs about your actions. Your soul contains your conscience. What you think about yourself is based upon what your conscience thinks about what you do and who you are. If you act contrary to your inner voice, you betray your *'self'* – the trinity of body, mind and soul. How can you like yourself if you betray your soul, the most intricate and intimate part of yourself? No amount of externally created self-esteem can bring peace to internal betrayal.

If your intention is pure your soul instructs you how to act in accordance with your intention. If you ignore the direction of the soul you create a spiritual schism. Spiritual illness – being out of touch with yourself and betraying your conscience – is at the root of most physical illness. Your unconscious and subconscious self manifests physical illness to stop your ego-generated striving and inspire you to seek a balanced path.

When we are rejected, threatened, abused or seduced away from our authentic self, our ego steps in to protect us. The unconscious and subconscious self is formed and our true self is hidden for safe-keeping. Thus, our ego becomes invested in the maintenance of our unconscious and subconscious habits, and can impede the expression of our authentic self. Until we find the courage to be authentic we will continue to feel unfulfilled. Being authentic takes courage. The reward is the realization that what we've been born to do in this life has not been done before. Being unique then takes on a completely different meaning.

Each person has a truth or set of beliefs. Your teachers, books, friends or family may have influenced these beliefs, but each person's truth is unique. We hold our deepest truths dear to our hearts. To identify your truth, start by looking at what you have always believed, particularly if your teachers, books, friends or family *didn't* believe these things. Being true to yourself means acknowledging all the ways in which you are different from others. That part of you that says *I believe something different* is your true self, the self you must befriend.

I have a great Dad. He taught me early in life to examine my values. I was six when he explained that money is not a goal in life. That's a great teaching, because if you agree money isn't the goal in life, you have to decide what is. You have to decide what is important to you and fill in the blank with something else. If money and the things it can buy aren't the goal, what is? This forced me to find value in the intangible aspects of life.

Often we have been rejected or threatened for being ourselves. We learn it is safer to hide our truth and focus on the popular culture of the day, or what our family, friends or partner believes is important.

Yogi Bhajan said many people will face what he termed *'cold depression.'* In this state you become frozen even to yourself. A person in cold depression is almost unreachable. Cold depression is caused by a combination of self-hatred caused by repeatedly violating your conscience, and your ego's drive to control the future.

If your mind is constantly creating a list of things you *'should'* do, you get further and further behind. You get locked in – *I don't have time for this, I don't have time for that; I've got to do this, I've got to do that.* This doesn't leave much time to experience life or express yourself and certainly there's no *'joie de vivre'* – enjoyment of life.

Constant unhappiness creates a mental pressure that overloads the glandular system creating physical, mental or emotional illness. To heal the manifestation of illness which comes out of cold depression requires a change in your vibration or frequency.

Kundalini Yoga is a great remedy for cold depression because it creates a vibrant physical body by strengthening your electromagnetic field (your aura and arcline). Kundalini Yoga also develops intuition – the sixth sense – or what Yogi Bhajan called the *'self-sensory'* self. When you develop your self-sensory self it gives you an awareness of yourself and the voice of your soul. It gives you an awareness of action and reaction. Your intuition begins to work accurately with your mental aspect to calculate the outcome of any action. You understand right from wrong and you begin to get into a flow of righteous action. As you move into this flow and get better and better at it, your self-sensory awareness becomes more sophisticated. It begins to not only tell you about you, it begins to tell you about me. The way it tells you about me is because *if you know your soul, you know every soul.*

Inside you is a system as complex as the world around you. We know the ecosystems on Earth are so complex it is impossible to know the ramification of every change we make. The same is true inside of you. You have a complex dynamic ecology going on all the time within and around your physical body.

We know about the extinction of species, but we don't look at human qualities that are becoming extinct like a cozy home and a nurturing society. In New Mexico where I live there were once forests full of trees. While it's gorgeous to see the red rocks and juniper that exist now, there is no longer grass as high as a horse's belly. They used to trap beaver from New Mexico to Mazatlan a few hundred years ago. Since then this entire ecology has changed drastically, and few people remember what has been lost. Just so, what it is to be human and nurturing is becoming extinct in our society.

When we are born our body ecology is like a rain forest. By the time you are an adult, caught up in everyday routines, you may feel you are living in a spiritual desert. Your body has become depleted because you haven't been exercising, eating right or doing yoga. No one taught you how to truly care for your body, mind and soul, much less all ten bodies. Without this training you end up in trouble, seeking a way to find balance.

Truth is whatever heals. When I first heard Yogi Bhajan talk about this, I dismissed it. Over time I came to firmly believe this concept is of the utmost importance in the healing process. If you have a thought and it's not making you better, it's not true for you. *Truth is whatever heals* – it's whatever nurtures, brings strength, independence, wholeness, infinity, and regeneration.

I don't believe you find yourself. I don't believe you create yourself. I believe you make a nurturing environment, let yourself be and see what grows. You can create an environment of people who support you, love you, and care for you. You can find a job that nurtures you and makes you feel good about yourself. You can eat delicious healing food that gives rather than takes energy from your body. You can do yoga to create an internal agricultural paradise. By keeping the ten bodies in balance you can heal the self because most of the time illness is a manifestation of being out of sync with the voice of your soul.

Chapter 5

THE VOICE OF THE SOUL

The soul body is a very small electromagnetic structure you can think of as a nugget of truth.

— DR. SIRI ATMA

Chapter 5
THE VOICE OF THE SOUL

The soul body is a very small electromagnetic structure you can think of as a nugget of truth.

If we think of the Infinite as the embodiment of all that is pure and true then each individual soul is a small piece of the Infinite; a small nugget of truth and purity. Within the soul is the personality of each human being. Our core loves and values are contained within our soul.

The voice of the soul is very clear. It speaks only of right and wrong and it does not defend itself. An easy way to distinguish the voice of the soul from other thoughts is to first remove all analytic thought. You'll be left with neurosis, phobia, delusion, and the voice of the soul. How do you tell the voice of the soul from neurosis, phobia, and delusion? The soul will always tell you what is right or wrong; *the rest will be fear based.*

> *Doubt has a fear, intuition never has a fear.*
> — YOGI BHAJAN

When we follow the voice of the soul we live a life of purity. We may still encounter pain and suffering but we can use the mind to calculate the best way to manifest the voice of the soul. We can assess the control our ego has over us by observing what our mind is calculating. If we are using our mind to figure out how to obey our conscience we are following the voice of our soul. If our mind is constantly preoccupied with achieving personal desires we are following the voice of our ego.

If you don't listen to your soul, you're ignoring yourself. If you don't follow your soul, you're betraying yourself. When someone betrays you, you don't like them. When you betray yourself, you won't like yourself either. There's no way to have positive self-esteem without being in touch with the voice of your soul.

There is no difference between our conscience and the voice of our soul; they are one and the same. Each individual has a different conscience. It does not matter what another person's conscience allows them to do. The only thing that matters is following what you believe is right and wrong. When you begin to follow what is right and wrong for you, you begin your spiritual journey.

We don't need direction from an outside source. We can follow our conscience all the way to God because our conscience is the voice of the Infinite within us. Following our conscience can be a scary thing. It helps if we have a nurturing environment where we can be who we truly are.

Religions initially are formed by groups of people who find they have common spiritual goals. A religious teacher or founder is someone who has traversed the terrain that the followers are about to embark upon. The spiritual teacher's job is to move students around spiritual pitfalls. Interestingly the largest pitfall we encounter on a spiritual path is our own spiritual ego. Spiritual ego occurs when we seek social recognition for our spiritual accomplishments.

Religions align us with ourselves when they nurture us to follow our conscience. When we listen to the conscience of others and not our own we lose our Godhead because the voice of our soul is the voice of God. There is no difference between God and our soul. The soul resides in the subtle body, so one thing you can do to hear the voice of the soul more clearly is work on your subtle body.

One of the most memorable things about Yogi Bhajan was his unwavering faith that God would support him. It was fabulous to witness his trust in the Infinite and see that he was always covered. One day I was explaining a medical course of action to him in an effort to get him to follow it. He was not swayed. He said, "Now we know the probability; let's see what God wants." He trusted the Infinite would cover the gap between the analytic probability and the voice of his soul. With the dawn of each day, he was proven right.

I did my undergraduate degree in Computer Science and Philosophy & Religion. From a Western point of view, philosophy, the study of the meaning of life, is conceptual in nature. Conversely, from an Eastern point of view philosophy is gained purely through experience.

Yoga appealed to me because I was looking for ways of breaking free from the mental patterns I was stuck in. I knew intuitively that yoga would help me. Through experience I confirmed that *yoga is actually about self-purification.* You can adjust your ten bodies by doing yoga, and in the process, change your karma and destiny.

> *All I know is that it doesn't matter what I teach, once the arcline and aura coincide to be blue and a golden twinge, job is done. Then it's time to go home. It means that day the purification has happened.*
>
> – YOGI BHAJAN

The bottom line is what Yogi Bhajan told me, "Now we know the probability; let's see what God wants." The mind is constantly calculating probability, constantly deciding what the odds are for this or that outcome. If you listen to your soul and let go of all calculation, you can sit, wait, and see what God wants. An important part of yoga is developing the capacity to wait. I can still hear my teacher's advice: "Patience pays."

Yoga allows you to break free of the mind so you can experience a state of elevated consciousness. When I first started yoga I said, "Wow, this stuff is so great, I'll be liberated in 3 years!" The teacher looked at me and said, "We'll be lucky to get you in Full Lotus in 3 years!" And he was right; he had experience.

Yogi Bhajan taught that there is a vast difference between knowledge and wisdom: *experience.* You can apply yoga and meditation to answer your questions and solve the things you puzzle over. *Give it time.* No matter how quickly you try to progress, wisdom and understanding come in their own time.

Each of us begins the journey by following our truth. The soul communicates to us by saying this is right and this is wrong, in the now. It doesn't say for how long. When we talk about the truth, we must realize it is expressed both as a thought and as an underlying vibration. Individual thoughts have a truth in time and space, while the source of the truth, the vibration, is timeless.

I am going to segue here a little bit. I started yoga not only to break free of mental blocks but also because of my ego. I was interested in spiritual knowledge. I had heard that yogis could do incredible feats of healing. I set out to become a spiritual healer. After several years of practicing yoga, I discovered that life is not about outcomes; life is about purity, about how purely you act. Yoga and meditation allow you to listen to what your consciousness tells you. It also gives you the ability to act on this newfound awareness.

> *Purity is for helping others. Your purity is the greatest ornamentation and gift which you can share with others. Just by being pure you can transform another person. You don't have to utter a word, just be pure, pure at heart. It is an art in itself which can help everybody. It is the subtlety of self.*
>
> – YOGI BHAJAN

Once you are practicing yoga, you develop an awareness of action and reaction. You can see spiritual clouds growing on the horizon. You may be aware that the Infinite has covered you up to this point, but you know it's not going to cover you any longer and you change your actions so you don't have to face the consequences. Your awareness clues you in.

Often we become lazy and do only enough to keep an unpleasant consequence we can sense on the horizon. Sometimes I would do that – I would do just enough homework, or just enough yoga, to stay out of trouble. That's a dangerous game to play when it concerns keeping illness at bay, because if you do it too much it can create a huge storm. By the time the illness manifests physically in your body, you are a long way from the *'clouds on the horizon'* phase.

As we pass through the stages of spiritual development, we begin to see that our soul's path is the same as every other soul's path. There are no spiritual shortcuts when it comes to choosing what is right. It definitely helps to be around other people who choose to follow their conscience. You'll find that consciousness is contagious!

Yogi Bhajan said, "The only difference between spiritual teachers is that some leave the path a mystery, while others explain it with mastery." He explained the path with consummate mastery. While this definitely helped his students see the traps and pitfalls, handholds and lifts along the way, the choice is still ours whether or not to pursue the path. "What type of teacher am I if I cannot teach you to initiate yourself?" Yogi Bhajan would ask. This leads back to the question of life we all encounter at some time or another: *Who am I, and what is the purpose of my life?*

There comes a point on the spiritual path where we give in to the will of the Infinite and just *'Be, to be.'* This is shorthand for saying, *Okay, here I am on Earth. I will stop trying to be. I will just be what I am.* What is higher than that? *'Be, to be.'* Outcomes are less important than being authentic to yourself.

Fulfillment comes when we act according to the voice of our soul, our authentic self. Learning to express ourselves and fulfill our life's purpose takes the same degree of concentration as it takes to paint a masterpiece. We can look at thousands of brush strokes in a Van Gogh painting or a single brush stroke in Oriental calligraphy and feel the same sense of inner peace and perfection. In both works of art, we experience the pure expression of the artist's authentic self. We continue on the spiritual path, not to gain social recognition or self-esteem, but because the *'spiritual path'* is each of us being who we are. Now instead of painting a picture as an expression of our inner self, our very existence becomes the expression of our being. The subtlety and refinement with which we express this defines our spiritual progress.

Chapter 6

ANGLES & TRIANGLES

Yoga is a science of angles and triangles.

–YOGI BHAJAN

Chapter 6
ANGLES & TRIANGLES

Yoga is a science of angles and triangles.

This is the first thing I ever learned from Yogi Bhajan. Why is this important? The Earth's core is as hot as the surface of the Sun, and around it there is a huge inner sphere of iron which forms a magnetic field. As the Earth rotates it generates an electromagnetic field which ultimately runs all life on Earth. In Kundalini Yoga the angles and triangles of the limbs are very specific as our arms and legs act as antennae. Moving the limbs through our electromagnetic field powerfully affects all ten bodies, especially the aura and arcline.

Each of the ten human bodies is significantly interactive with the others. They must all go through the circuit of the mind to coordinate, and all are dependent on one thing – *prana*. Prana is the life force which charges the molecules and cells of our body.[2]

Within each molecule a tremendous amount of activity occurs between electrons and protons and this constitutes our magnetic field or magnetic psyche. We each have a magnetic psyche and we live under a magnetic field. Kundalini Yoga enables us to control our magnetic psyche so we can have strength of mind and body and a clear identity of self. We can change our reality by practicing yoga to create a direct relationship between the finite and Infinity.[3]

The beauty of Kundalini Yoga is that it is a technique to move the psyche through a physical action.

— YOGI BHAJAN

There are three celestial bodies that influence the human body: the Earth, the Sun and the Moon. They exert their influence through their electromagnetic fields and their tidal effects and solar winds. It is fascinating to realize that over 5,000 years ago, mankind understood these forces well enough to develop a sophisticated system of yoga to utilize these energies to create maximal functioning in human beings.

The electromagnetic fields of the Earth and Sun communicate and affect our energy levels daily. The psyche of the Earth changes during the ambrosial hours when the magnetic strength of the day begins. You change from subtle to active in preparation for the day's activities from 3:00 a.m. to 6:00 a.m.; from 6:00 a.m. to 3:00 p.m. your activity continues; and from 3:00 p.m. to 6:00 p.m. you and every living thing on Earth begins to slow down.[4]

Kundalini Yoga moves energy through the body by capturing the pranic electromagnetic force via breath techniques in which the lungs and pranic body interact. This strengthens the electromagnetic field around us, i.e. our aura and arcline, which creates a vibrant physical body. Auric changes affect the mind and arcline, while arcline changes affect the soul and subtle body. These changes also improve the way we think, communicate and perceive life, by impacting the focus of our thoughts, or what the yogis and mystics call our awareness.

As human beings we have fiber, we have an electromagnetic field, we have emotions, we have feelings – it's a circuitry of life. It's a dance of ten trillion cells and the beauty of it is that we are dancing in such harmony.

— YOGI BHAJAN

Each cell within our body is alive with a perceptive intelligence called *cell-to-cell communication*. Awareness is the subset of communication on which our attention is focused. Yoga strengthens the aura and arcline and through interconnectivity, creates electrical and glandular mental activity which shifts our awareness.

All the bodies are interconnected and their relationships have a profound effect on our state of mind. For example, unless the pranic body is in harmony with the subtle body and the subtle body is in harmony with the aura, it doesn't matter who you are, you will be nervous.[5] You can attempt to shift the focus of your awareness with thought control, but unless you adjust the aura and arcline, such changes are fleeting.

Chapter 7

THE TEN
BODIES
IN-DEPTH

The soul body is also called the spiritual body.

– DR. SIRI ATMA

Chapter 7
THE TEN BODIES IN-DEPTH

THE SOUL

The soul body is also called the spiritual body.

The soul is our timeless body which contains our being, consciousness and personality. The five constituents of the body are the tattvas: ether, air, fire, water and earth. Your soul resides in every atom of your tattvas. The combined weight of the soul is a quarter of an ounce or less.

The other nine bodies were given to serve the soul, the real subject of life. With the light of the soul, the mind and the other bodies progress spiritually. You must connect with your soul in this lifetime in order to achieve anything majestic or divine.

The soul tells us what is right and wrong for us:

> *Taking this action would be a good thing to do.* Or, *This would be harmful.*

Your soul has nothing to do with pain and pleasure; it is the sensitivity of your consciousness which is the source of your happiness. While yoga can directly heal the mind and body, it has its most powerful effects on the soul. When we change what the soul attracts, we can begin to heal our mental, emotional and physical illness. Yoga has the power to speed up our spiritual evolution as the postures work on the aura and arcline, deeply affecting our soul body.

THE TRIPLE MIND: NEGATIVE, POSITIVE, NEUTRAL

Happiness can only be achieved if you have control of your mind. Your mind is meant to be your servant; if it becomes your master, you don't have a chance. The mental body is very strong – it's a triple body and cannot be allowed to control us.

> *The mind has three aspects: negative, positive and neutral. Learn what a neutral statement is. That is the way your perpetual endurance will develop, you will never defeat yourself, your fuse will not go off.*
>
> – YOGI BHAJAN

THE NEGATIVE MIND

The job of your negative mind is to calculate risk and protect you. If your negative mind is out of balance you cannot think about yourself or protect yourself through your intelligence. The negative mind must think negatively about anything you know, hear, and see. Whenever a thought comes to you or whenever someone speaks to you, your negative mind's role is to say:

> *Wait a minute. What is this person saying? Why? Am I reading it right?*

The negative mind negates everything that comes to you no matter how positive it may be; it happens automatically. It starts surveying the situation and tells you what is negative in it. Even if a proposal is very much in your favor your negative mind will tell you:

> *You don't have the time and energy to carry out the job. It's not worth it.*

If you are not in touch with your negative mind and you mis-understand its role, this barrage of negative thoughts can make you fearful and cause unnecessary doubt – the worst enemy of the human. When you have doubt in your mind, your subtle body is not relating to your soul. The healing process is about unifying the subtle and soul bodies, which leaves no room for doubt.

THE POSITIVE MIND

The positive mind calculates benefit. The job of your positive mind is to tell you what is positive in the negative. If you do not use the positive mind this way, it starts working very unfortunately for you – it takes information from your subconscious and your memory to support the thoughts of the negative mind. You have a storehouse of tragedies in your life. Your positive mind can pull up the past and lay it on you like this:

> *Ten years ago we had a proposal like this and it was a bad experience. We suffered many losses.*

When out of balance your positive mind can unload your subconscious memory, pull out the garbage and double it. When your positive mind brings up your total human experience in this way, it prevents you from making the correct decision. You can only live happily if you build a positive mind and it does not pull out the past to enforce your negative mind.

The role of the positive mind is to tell you all the beneficial aspects of a situation. If your positive mind cannot do this you cannot experience joy and bliss and your ability to achieve is greatly diminished.

THE NEUTRAL MIND

You have a third mental body, the neutral mind, whose job is to guide you and tell you what you should do. You *must* know the positive of the negative and the neutral of the positive and negative, so you can compute and act right.

The neutral mind evaluates risk and benefit; it was given so we can know how things relate to time and space. Every thought which is realized goes from the negative mind to the positive mind, and it must go to the neutral mind to give you a comprehensive answer of time, space, your environment and you. If you have a comprehensive mind you are never wrong; otherwise you'll never be right.

Without the neutral mind you cannot be consistently constant and know who you are. Instead you'll think:

> I have to compete. If I don't do better than everyone else, I will not get the promotion.

This is not neutral. The principle of the neutral mind is dutiful:

> I will not let myself down; I will not let anyone else down. I will create a win-win situation.

If your neutral mind can preserve one leading thought and you do not condemn yourself, whatever you need shall be provided.

THE PHYSICAL BODY

The physical body has the capacity to correlate your activities so you can come through; it was given to share feelings and emotions. We can see the physical body. We can identify with the five senses of sight, sound, taste, touch and smell. These senses plus the sensations of pain and pleasure are the primary ways in which the physical body communicates to us.

The physical body cannot work for you if you do not discipline it. You cannot put anything in your body which over or under stimulates you. Eat only what can be eliminated in twenty-four hours. How do you know if the food you eat will be eliminated in twenty-four hours? At the end of your meal eat a few slices of beets; they will turn your stool red.

You need to exercise and sweat forty-five minutes to an hour a day to regulate the chakras and stimulate the glands, the guardians of your health. Exercise is a must for you whether you are rich or poor.

One hour of mental exercise, meditation, is also required. In meditation you become calm and open yourself to the vastness of infinity. By consciously concentrating on your breath of life you regulate and rejuvenate your body. You must not start your day without taking care of your mind.

Just being physically beautiful is not enough. You have to match your physical beauty with your mental beauty. You can put on makeup, but you will still look ugly if the light body, your soul, is not radiating through your skin. It doesn't matter how much makeup you use, you will look unhealthy. If your pranic body is not in sync with your physical body, you will look grumpy. If your auric body doesn't balance your physical body, you can't achieve anything in life. And if your subtle body does not collaborate with your physical body, you will end up lying all the time; you cannot relate to being pure.

Your source of unhappiness is when you do not coordinate the ten bodies and you think you have just a physical body. Then when your physical body fails you get depressed instead of calling on the other nine bodies. To have mastery of the self you have to train your physical body to know all ten bodies.

There are ten bodies, ask them all. They are your friends, they are with you. Ask their opinion, get it together and then decide – that's called conscious decision.

– YOGI BHAJAN

THE ARCLINE

The arcline is the halo around you that stretches from earlobe to earlobe. It guides and controls your aura; it was given as a shield, a protection. Your arcline should alert you. It produces your destiny and destiny creates its parallel, fate.

It is the strength of your arcline by which you live. The strength of your body, your strength of doing, and your strength of projection lie in your arc body. The arcline tells you about circumstances distant to you in time and space, for example:

> *You are running out of good fortune. A bad event is headed your way.*

Or you may get a message such as: *You should go visit your mother.* There may be an insistence about the message which gives you the impression there is more to it. If your arcline is strong and your awareness of the arcline is strong the messages you receive will be more complete.

You can see your arcline when you concentrate in certain meditations. Your arcline can be silver-white, bluish-white, white, gray, pink, or green. If your arc body is not within the color range you should have, you will be afraid. If your arc body is weak you can't respond to anything; you have no response to reality.

Your arcline can be reflective or dull, which reflects your capacity. It is a thermometer of your total energy. Any breaks in the arcline show weakness or disease and overlaps mean the disease is serious.

Creative energy travels through your arcline. Calmness is seen in your arcline. That is why you are called a human being. *Human being: Now, you are the light. Hue means the light.* You emit light which touches the boundary of other people's arcline and aura. This is what is called grace – the best facet of a human.

THE AURA

Most of the time you are guided by your outer personality, your aura. The aura records almost everything that happens to your psyche. The pain and pleasure you experience are recorded in your aura, your akashic record. The aura protects you from other people's negativity, and gives you sensitivity to your environment; it was given so you can reflect yourself.

The aura tells you about circumstances in present time. It talks to you about things close to you in time and space, such as:

> *This direction is safe; that direction is dangerous.* Or, *This person is trying to undermine me.*

A strong aura and arcline enable us to have a better sense of our own identity. While our arcline protects us from the thoughts and projections of people distant from us, our aura protects us from the thoughts and projections of people in our presence. If you are aware of other people's thoughts more than your own in the presence of other people it means you have a weak aura.

Sometimes the power of your aura is so strong it moves faster than you. No human being is weak unless his power over his aura is weak. When the aura is small, three and a half feet on each side, you are just an animal. Your aura has been condensed and as a result your animal nature can cause you to act to the point of brutality. The human body can have an aura of up to nine feet on each side. When your aura is expanded it enhances your strength and health, and your angelic subtle nature. It is the density of your aura which makes you act incorrectly, and it is the vastness and subtlety of your aura which makes you act right and makes you beautiful.

THE PRANIC BODY

The pranic body is the electromagnetic body of life. The pranic body gives life to the physical body and is connected to it through the breath; it was given so we can live. Your prana, or life energy, penetrates through your radiant body fifteen times a minute on average. There is a strong relationship between the pranic and physical bodies. Yogis have used this relationship for thousands of years to cure illness and lengthen life. When your breath is not deep enough to correspond with the needs of the body, your relationships, your behavior and your life will all be out of balance.

The pranic body communicates mostly with the mind and lungs, enhancing health through control of the breath. It does not contribute thoughts per se, but a competent yogi is aware of what the pranic body is communicating when practicing breath control. In particular, the yogi experiences the *'rise of the Kundalini'* while holding the breath out.

Without prana, the physical body cannot hold the soul. Each soul is granted a certain number of pranic breaths and once you finish that quota your soul enters your subtle body and leaves. When the relationship between the soul and pranic bodies is permanently broken, life comes to an end.

THE SUBTLE BODY

The subtle body gives the capacity to learn quickly and relate to the nuances of life; it was given so we can understand. Within the subtle body is the awareness of the soul, i.e. self-awareness. The subtle body is larger than the soul, very transparent, light, and etheric in nature. The subtle body can be thought of as the body of refinement. It is subtlety which contains Infinity.

If you create a very powerful subtle body you will understand the subtleties of life, and you will never ever be trapped in perversion. You will understand the grassroots reality of everything. It is the subtlety of life which people trust.

Thoughts from the subtle body refine the input from the soul. The soul may say:

Taking this action would be good.

The subtle body looks at what is requested and then makes distinctions:

This is good, but this would be better, and this would be the best course of action.

The subtle body is the guardian of spirit, health and life. It is the most powerful of all your bodies and is strengthened by meditation. Anytime you work on self-refinement you work on the subtle body. You can significantly improve your connection with your soul through music, art, creating a beautiful home or dressing regally. Refined art, refined acts, refined speech, will all put you nearer to the soul. If you become very, very subtle, you are very near to your soul. That is a simple way of reaching God consciousness.

THE RADIANT BODY

The radiant body's magnetic attraction gives us courage; it was given so we can influence and prosper. You are born to be positive and enjoy nothing but positive things in life. It will come to you provided you are balanced in your identity. When your shield is on, you are bright and beautiful. When your radiant body is shining like the Sun there is no way you can ever be wrong. Your radiant body doesn't act right when it is clouded by fear.

Good luck comes to you, not because you deserve it, not because you want it, not because you are beautiful and not because you asked for it. It comes to you because of your electromagnetic field and the radiance of your tenth body. You don't have to speak a word when your radiant body is effective. Sometimes you misunderstand and think, *I did it, I attracted it, I got it.* That is not true. It is your confidence and the strength of the radiant body which brings success. The physical body is just a basement; the radiant body is the top story, the tenth floor.

That's what Kundalini Yoga is about; it builds strength in you. You become you. All your fears, conflicts and duality go away. Your reality starts coming, and things come to you because you are very attractive. The attraction is not you; it is your absolutely radiant body. The radiant body is a shining armor around you for both protection and attraction. Its radiance depends on how deeply you consume prana each day by breathing deeply.

 The first nine bodies are mostly receptive – they receive information and communicate to us. Our tenth body, the radiant body, is the natural result of the electromagnetic activity of the other nine bodies. In order for there to be a natural balance our bodies must project as well as receive. The radiant body is the electromagnetic projection of the essence of the other nine bodies. It is through the radiant body that our inner radiance is communicated to the world.

THE TEN BODIES

You may think that you have five senses, but actually you have *eight* senses. Five are contained in the physical body: the senses to see, hear, taste, smell and touch. Your sixth sense is the intuitive sense which is within your auric body. The seventh is common sense which is within your subtle body. The eighth sense, your sense of humor, comes from your pranic body. Yogi Bhajan said that your sense of humor is your best friend through every difficulty in life; without it there is no way out.

When you know the role each body plays you can identify which body is communicating. This is useful because it adds context to information that might otherwise leave you puzzled. If you have no context on which to base certain thoughts you may ascribe them to intuition or instinct or ignore them all together. Problems occur when the mind claims authorship for all thought. Ideally the mind serves as a mental calculator to consciously guide you. When you know how to use your mind under the guidance of your soul and not the ego, you can balance the waves of thoughts and feelings that continuously arise. But when the mind is subject to the ego it calculates how to avoid what it fears, how to get what it wants, and how to get even with whatever gets in its way.

Chapter 8

WHAT TO DO WITH THE MIND

Your mind is a link between Infinity and you.

— DR. SIRI ATMA

Chapter 8
WHAT TO DO WITH THE MIND

Your mind is a link between Infinity and you.

When the soul has to separate from Infinity, it wants to know how it can connect with God while on Earth. The answer is *through your mind.* Your mind can take you to Infinity and your mind can take you into the pit of negativity.

Whenever a thought comes to you, whenever you speak to someone or someone speaks to you, first your negative mind plays its role and thinks, *Am I reading it right? What is the purpose of this call? Why is this person inviting me?* The job of your negative mind is to protect you and it does so by negating everything. It creates fear and gives you unnecessary negative alertness.[6]

Your positive mind can act as a super-negative force, bringing up all your old memories to consider, *John did this, Thomas did this to me, Henry did this.* If you cannot pull the thoughts from the negative mind to the positive mind you will be governed by fear. Fear is the worst thing to live with because it can destroy every part of your life. Fear will turn to vengeance and vengeance unchecked can lead to ungodly acts. If you can pull yourself from your negative mind to your positive mind you will enter a new horizon.

If you master your mind, you master the whole universe because once you master your mind and bring it to neutrality the Universal mind will serve you.

— YOGI BHAJAN

Our mind gives us 1,000 thoughts per blink of the eye. Many of our thoughts paralyze us with fear, doubt and insecurity. We have this sense that we are out of touch with ourselves, but we are not sure what our '*self*' is.

You can talk to your mind and it will obey. If it doesn't and thoughts come and start rallying around just start breathing consciously. You will be surprised how fast you can change once you utilize the breath of life. If you have the practice to breathe through your left nostril you can get out of any mental confusion in two seconds. The moment you start breathing through your left nostril, your elementary self comes into play and the totality of your mind becomes one and adds the radiant shield of your body. You will immediately feel very positive rather than angry and reactive. [7]

You must understand that the mind consumes massive quantities of your physical body's energy. In an effort to conserve energy, the mind limits the amount of background information you need to process, and focuses only on things that change rapidly or that you perceive as a threat. When you are faced with a potential threat, real or imagined, your mind can become locked in a '*do-loop.*' A do-loop is a computer programming term for when a computer freezes. The computer is told to repeat a task until a certain condition is reached, then to exit the loop and move to the next step. Occasionally the computer will encounter a situation the programmer didn't envision. When it enters this loop, it is unable to find a way to exit and it freezes. Similarly, a do-loop can happen in the brain when something occurs that puts us *over-the-top.* Our mind freezes in order to shut down and regain stability before we can proceed.

Physiologically our mental state is controlled by the flow of messages between neurons in the brain and hormones released by the body. Major hormones that affect the way we think and feel include estrogen, testosterone, and thyroid hormone. These hormones are controlled by the pineal, pituitary, thalamus and hypothalamus glands. The pineal gland controls your sense of self-worth and your self-identity. The pituitary controls growth hormone and thyroid hormone release in both men and women as well as the menstrual cycle in women.

The thalamus allows processing of neurological activity into glandular hormonal activity. The effects of hormones produced by the hypothalamus and pituitary affect us for days or weeks. The cost of producing these hormones is significantly less than the energy consumed by continual neurological activity, so hormones are a huge cost-savings to the body.

The hypothalamus receives feedback on the amount of hormone produced in the body and ensures that the glandular system is not swayed by large but relatively short bursts of mental or emotional activity. The result is that our glandular system creates a stabilizing effect on the mind in terms of beliefs and emotions. When we are trying to change, some of our mental opposition is generated by the stabilizing effect of our glandular system.

If you do not feel safe and secure your body and mind have difficulty entering a recuperative cycle. Many of my patients tell me that their minds are rarely at ease. Potential threats are ever present – from fear of nuclear war to fear of rejection by a loved one. Fear and worry can sap the body's strength by causing mental fatigue which uses greater amounts of sugar and neurotransmitters than when the mind is at rest. Fear and worry cause physical fatigue by over-stimulating your adrenal glands, which also impairs the recuperative cycle.

The body must have a period of stress-free time in which it can relax and rebuild itself. This is difficult in a culture like ours where stimulation, competition and accomplishment rule our lives. We don't know why we're here and we don't know where we're going. We pursue social recognition, monetary security, and pleasures of every variety. We are driven by subconscious impulses and controlled by our minds. We are aware that there is more to life and we would like to find out what this 'more' is, so we decide to gain control of our life by controlling our mind with our mind.

Trying to control your mind with your mind will not work and there are basic biological reasons for this. The first is that part of the mind's function is memory. Our mind would not remember things well if it changed too easily. So our mind has very sophisticated systems to keep things *as they are.* Maintaining the status quo has survival benefit – it allows the brain to focus on what is changing instead of everything at once. This helps the body conserve energy.

The Earth, the Moon and the Sun exert their influence on us in the following ways:

> – the pineal gland, the master gland, cycles with the solar year. It also provides a slow guiding rhythm to the more rapidly fluctuating lunar and earthly glandular cycles;

> – the pituitary gland cycles with the lunar month. The pituitary rotates and vibrates in harmony with the rotation of the Earth and Moon, the daily and monthly clocks;

> – the electromagnetic field of the Earth's atmosphere changes around us under the influence of photons from the Sun;

> – the Moon's gravitational field changes the water element in our bodies daily;

> – moonlight affects the moon center in men, i.e. their emotional state;

> – the solar effect of light stimulates our brain through our eyes and the porous bone of the forehead, allowing light to stimulate the pineal gland;

> – sunlight affects our nervous system through the eyes and creates a longing within to see or know more about the world around us; in the same way moonlight excites us to know more about our own inner self and being.

The hypothalamus acts as a negative feedback switch, controlling the maximum amount of total end hormone in the body as well as the effect of neurological input from the thalamus on the pituitary. The human body goes through daily, weekly/monthly, and yearly/decade cycles that are hormonally regulated by the brain's master glands. These glands are affected by our thoughts in an aggregate way. Thus the hypothalamus acts as a buffer to make sure that a short burst of excessive emotional or mental activity does not throw our whole system out of balance.

The glandular system is really what maintains the status quo of our mental activity. So to change the way we think and act, we must change the secretion of the glands in the brain. This system is a two-way positive feedback system, in that depression causes glandular secretions which maintain a depressed state of mind, while glandular changes that create depression (such as seasonal affective disorder) create mental changes that maintain glandular depression.

There are many ways you can improve the body's glandular secretions to prevent or alleviate depression. You can move to a climate where there is more sunlight. You can change your diet to include chemicals that improve mental performance, stimulate or relax your nervous system, and improve your mood by affecting the temporal lobe of the brain, limbic system and thalamus. You can include more physical activity to increase the secretion of endorphins.

Changing your social environment is also beneficial. You can choose friends who have a positive influence on you. You can consciously think positive thoughts and seek out positive experiences. You can create an uplifting spiritual environment with inspiring pictures, soothing music and aromatherapy. Sandalwood is known as a very uplifting fragrance and is good for mental clarity.

Yoga is the most powerful way to circumvent the blocks of the mind. By changing the aura and arcline with the pranic and physical bodies, changes in the soul, mental, subtle and radiant bodies are produced. This results in permanent changes in our glandular system, which can lock in positive changes in our mental state. This is the best way to positively change the mind without mental confrontation.

We have come to this world to fulfill our spiritual dreams. But it is normally seen that we end up fulfilling our earthly dreams. The mind is the availability through which you can swing from one choice to the other.

– YOGI BHAJAN

Chapter 9

MEDITATION

Intention is what dominates the outcome in both yoga and meditation.

— DR. SIRI ATMA

Chapter 9
MEDITATION

Intention is what dominates the outcome in both yoga and meditation.

Meditation is different from prayer. In meditation we listen, merge into the divine, and allow the divine to merge in us; in prayer we communicate with the divine. After preparing the body to receive divine thought through yoga, meditation aligns our vibration with the divine. Meditation brings inspiration and understanding that changes our desires, actions and reactions and thus our karma. It gives us the experience of divine will – the understanding that everything is perfectly created. We realize that God is the true Doer of everything so we can relax and stop striving.

> *Meditation is the creative control of self so that the Infinite can talk to you.*
>
> – YOGI BHAJAN

God is in the Heavens, but God is also right inside us guiding our actions. We can listen or not, that is our choice. If we listen to our conscience, we learn that life is not about outcomes, it is about doing the right thing. It does not matter if we are rich or poor, young or old, healthy or unhealthy – what does matter is that we do our best according to our conscience.

The act of meditation affects our physical and mental bodies through the glandular system. It affects our mind and emotions through vibration and communication with the soul. We repeat a mantra that reminds our soul of its Infinity, creating a resonance in our living space, our body and minds. This reminder, for example, *'Happy am I, Healthy am I, Holy am I'* clues the soul into its true identity.

The act of meditation is practice. You practice meditation to learn to control the mind. You create a relationship with your mind – a relationship created between your magnetic field and that of the Universe. Meditation gives you intuition; it gives you a comprehensive mind. A comprehensive mind and happiness go together.[8]

> *The mind is beyond time and space. It is part of the Universal Mind. It is given to you as an instrument to serve you. What happened? It became your master and you became the servant. The mind becomes a monster when it becomes your master. The mind is an angel when it becomes your servant.*
>
> – YOGI BHAJAN

For years I had strict ideas about how a spiritual teacher should and shouldn't act. I held fixed images about what it was to be *'enlightened'* – based not on my experience, but upon books I had read. Internally I held Yogi Bhajan to these standards. In retrospect, it was the funniest thing. When I was around him, I had the highest spiritual experiences of my life. I applied his teachings and reached states of awareness I never thought possible. Despite this, for eighteen years I still did not think he knew enough to transform me!

I would choose which teachings to learn and practice. I would decide who I was and who I wasn't. I never let him touch me. On the other hand, if he were to deviate just once from my preconceived notion of how a saint should act, I would be out the door in 30 seconds. It finally occurred to me that if he had all this knowledge and had gone through the *'course'* himself, he probably knew what he was doing and I could let him carve me out. This began an entirely new level of spiritual growth for me, which would prove to be both exciting and challenging. As I said, I love to learn.

I realized that the minute you want out of your relationship with a Master, the game is over. Why? Because the minute you decide you can't keep up or you refuse to relinquish your ego, there really isn't any reason for the Teacher to continue teaching you. The whole point of the lesson is to learn that you are Infinite, that *'God and me, me and God, are one.'* In order to learn this, the Teacher must test you to the end, until you learn to overcome your weaknesses.

The job of a spiritual teacher is to give the student an impossible task and see how they fare. Your ego decides the task is impossible. To succeed at an impossible task, you must ignore the ego and surrender to the will of the Infinite. Surrendering to the Infinite is simply accepting that everything is the way it should be, and deciding that you are tired of trying to get your way. Instead you listen to the voice of the Infinite and follow that path. In this way your Teacher teaches you that true meditation is making that conscious decision and living it with each and every breath.

Chapter 10

ENLIGHTENMENT

During college I spent a year in India at the Golden Temple studying religion.

– DR. SIRI ATMA

Chapter 10
ENLIGHTENMENT

During college I spent a year in India at the Golden Temple studying religion.

My intention was to study the Sikh faith, but I became much more interested in how an *'Eastern'* religion would view western faiths. So I studied the Western religions as taught by Sikh philosophers. Sometime during that year I formed my "triangulation" view of religion: If three or more major world religions held a particular viewpoint, I concluded that there was a high probability of its validity. If two religions held the same view, then the idea probably had merit. If only one religion held a view, it might be a universal truth, but more likely it was a cultural belief. Once I discovered this way of viewing the similarities between religions, I could not understand why anyone would want to focus on their differences.

In Amritsar none of the shopkeepers talked about what faith another man followed. Instead, they asked, "Is he a good Christian? Is he a good Hindu? A good Buddhist, Sikh, Muslim or Jain?" There was an implicit understanding that any man honestly trying to improve himself could succeed with any faith. The megalomaniacal view that there is one true religion and one true way to enlightenment seems absurd especially when even within religions no one seems to agree. And in a country with as many religions as India, it doesn't make sense to cut yourself off from other religions; you would quickly find yourself in the minority.

During college, I met a man who taught me how to tune a Model A Ford. The closest

I have ever been to a Model A Ford is watching a parade! I realized that much of the knowledge I was acquiring during my *'higher education'* would not stand the test of time. How much of what I was learning would be of value to my great-grandchildren? I began to evaluate knowledge by its longevity. Most religions have stood the test of time. If you doubt the beauty of the founder of any religion, look at the flowering of culture that bloomed around the birth of that faith.

When I finished my medical residency, Yogi Bhajan sent me a short note: *Write and tell me what your plans are. Just remember, Española is God's mailing address.* I understood his subtle message – he thought it would be best if I moved to Española, New Mexico. I followed his advice. In Española there was a lot of medical work to be done and not much money for doing it, so I became philosophical about work and money. If I took the time to do a good job with preventative care I wouldn't make much money but in the long run more people would be healthy. If I spent more time answering patient questions, surely my patients would spread this information to their families and friends. I decided that this *'high touch, high face'* time would win the majority of my medical battles. I still believe this.

Seven or eight years later, I was driving home from work one day and a voice said to me, "You have now gained enough gratitude from others that you have paid for this human life. If you keep your nose clean from now until the end of your life you are through." I realized that the only true wealth you earn in this life is the gratitude of the people you have helped. I hadn't ended up in Beverly Hills making lots of money. Instead, I ended up in Española, where hearts are warm, and understanding and compassion are a necessity of life. I felt immensely rich, for the way I looked at it, I had earned a wealth of gratitude for relatively little effort. Yogi Bhajan said it this way:

The sacredness in life is when you go, you feel, and you touch and make somebody's day. Then what happens? One day you make one person's day, the next day you make 10 people's day and the third day you make 100 people's day. By the end of the month, you've made 10,000 people's day.

Soon you have 10,000 psycho-magnetic energies focusing at you, vibrating: 'He is a good man.' It's a mantra. It's a constant vibration. 'He is a good man.' Now bad cannot come near you...Power is in the remembrance... It is a psycho-magnetic communication.

– YOGI BHAJAN

An ocean wave is created when wind travels over water. When we meet *'enlightened'* beings, their radiance hits us like a wave, so we think that enlightenment will hit us like a wave as well. This is not the case. Enlightenment is something that we participate in every minute of every day. When I first started studying with Yogi Bhajan, I realized that I violated my conscience on a regular basis. Over time it happened less and less until I was following the voice of my soul virtually all the time. My equation for *'enlightenment'* became the following:

ENLIGHTENMENT = conscience (wind) over time (distance of water)

When the voice of our soul is known to us, over time a wave of enlightenment is created, not only for us, but for those around us. Enlightenment then can be seen as being one with the will of God, submitting to our conscience, following the voice of our soul, or being in touch with the Infinite. These are all ways of saying the same thing. Others are struck by the wave of enlightenment that emanates from a yogi who has followed the instruction of the Infinite over time.

There's a beauty in your presence. There's a beauty in your radiance. And that radiating of your psyche reaches out and communicates who you are.

– YOGI BHAJAN

I really believe that when we're looking at enlightenment it is equally difficult for everyone. Everyone has to go through the same spiritual stages and surpass them in the process of working on the spiritual illness of ego. There is a moment in our spiritual progress when we are satisfied with the way things are, and realize there isn't much else we desire.

We are interested in self-purification because this is what ultimately heals us and others. There are thousands of ways in which healing takes place – a thought, a word, a look, a gesture, a vibration of love. We can care for the physical body, but eventually we will leave it behind. We can seek our own happiness but in the end, the only happiness we find is in the service of others.

> *Kundalini Yoga is a householder's yoga. It is a yoga that allows an ordinary person to live in this world, experience the ecstasy of consciousness, and then use this consciousness to serve humanity.*
>
> – YOGI BHAJAN

Happiness comes from the power to sacrifice. The first thing we must sacrifice is our ego. Self-purification can be thought of as thinking only loving thoughts. I think of it as gaining control over fear and vengeance instead of letting them control me.

The soul has a natural healing ability, the same as our bodies and minds. Healing takes place when the soul lives in a nurturing environment, and realizes there is nothing to fear. Being surrounded by kind, loving people is one way to accomplish this. At some point, we must stop worrying about ourselves and just start serving. We can draw strength from the knowledge that we will never die and that the truth spoken by our soul lives forever.

What or who we are is not the main issue. Authenticity is. As our authenticity grows, we serve others simply by setting an example. No amount of freedom in a society frees us from ourselves. We enslave ourselves to the will of the ego. Enlightenment is freedom from that enslavement. How a person acts when freed from their ego is set by the needs of the souls around them. Enlightenment occurs when we have developed the inner strength and courage to face our anger and fear and serve all life.

Chapter 11
THE KNOWING

We have thoughts generated by communication from all ten bodies.

— DR. SIRI ATMA

Chapter 11
THE KNOWING

We have thoughts generated by communication from all ten bodies.

From this swirling of thoughts we focus on a small subset and from that subset we select only a few thoughts on which we act. Some of this selection is done rationally, some emotionally, some impulsively. In the background are components of trust, commitment, experience and learning. And the question in time and space is, *Do our actions calm the itchiness of our mind and result in satisfaction?*

We come to this Earth as a soul and subtle body combination. We obtain eight other bodies, and strive to make sense of the resulting jumble of thoughts. Before we gain a spiritual awareness of our self, we act reflexively, guided largely by the ego. How do we know if our thoughts are ego based? If we find that the thoughts driving our mind are calculating personal gain instead of mutual gain.

The most important *knowing* to be aware of is the conscience, or the voice of the soul. The hallmark of the soul's voice is that it does not give details, it just presents facts. *This is right and this is wrong.* Along with the facts is a knowing of why this is so.

The Piscean age, which we are leaving, is characterized by the statement, *If I believe then I will experience.* The Aquarian Age, which we are now entering, states, *I will experience and then I will believe.* The point of distinguishing the source of our thoughts is to know our ten bodies. We do not need to do yoga for years to experience the aura and arcline.

If we understand that certain thoughts are generated by the aura and the arcline, we begin to become more aware of them.

The whole point of *Waves of Healing* is to make you aware that what you are seeking is right in front of you. You don't need to go and spend a bunch of money to gain psychic abilities or mystic experiences, or to know your future. You already have the best guide within you.

> *When you are angry, frustrated, depressed and need counseling – sit down and meditate. Your mind will fight you, but don't lose your strength. Mind is your own child. Train it, don't cater to it. Your soul can come to you through the mind. The only thing that works is when you can see your own soul, your own light, through your mind.*
>
> – YOGI BHAJAN

I can tell you what your soul is like by reading your face, your energy, your aura and knowing the type of illness you are manifesting. I can sit quietly and listen to my soul and watch how you shift me when you enter my presence and thereby know where your soul is at, but how does this help you? I can't spend my whole life helping you listen to the voice of your soul. This is something that you must do for yourself.

People seeking spiritual experience go off track in many ways. The first is missing the spiritual experience they could be having right now. Life is not that good or that bad, it is what it is. You just need to relax, stop striving to become or to get, and just be. Be who you are. Enjoy it. If it were in your best interest for things to be different, they would be different.

Life is about learning that we do not have to act according to our ego in order to succeed. Death is about learning that there is no death, that we do in fact live forever. Who is it that is learning in this life – our body, our mind? No. Our soul is learning. All that life and death eventually teach our soul is we do not have to act and God will take care of us.

When we *know* in our hearts that our soul is the road to higher consciousness, we give up and say, *I am just so tired of doing, of acting, of hustling and hassling my way through life. I quit. I will no longer listen to my ego. Instead I will listen only to the voice of my soul.* If we are very lucky, we learn this early on and avoid a life-long struggle.

Chapter 12
SERENITY

When the soul finds its path it is in Saram Pad, the first stage on the spiritual path.

– DR. SIRI ATMA

Chapter 12
SERENITY

When the soul finds its path it is in Saram Pad, the first stage on the spiritual path.

I remember first learning about this and thinking, *There is no way that there are defined stages on the spiritual path. Everyone must have a separate path!* As I began to see medical illness as the result of spiritual separation from one's soul, I started to understand the spiritual path.

In Saram Pad, disturbed by an ever increasing awareness of the separation of our self from our soul, we begin to search for life's meaning. Once we find our path, the knowledge that we will be able to diminish the separation between our self and our soul brings joy and healing and provides motivation to 'keep-up.'

Karam Pad is the next stage on the spiritual path. The student has learned the techniques to heal the gap between self and soul, and begins to apply them. This is a time of Karam, or work. In this stage, the soul seeks peace while the ego is sure that the self will now become a great soul in the form of a saint, holy person, or healer. Seekers in this stage are proud of their spiritual accomplishments: *I prayed for everyone I know; I meditated for six hours; I haven't missed a day of spiritual practice for ten years.*

Those in Karam Pad mistake the spiritual practice for the goal, just as a young musician may be proud of memorizing a musical score and misunderstand that the goal of music is to inspire through the sense of sound. A young musician and inexperienced yogi may both develop skill at the expense of personal transcendence.

The next stage in transformation is Shakti Pad. In Shakti Pad, we begin to realize that the real purpose of life is to uplift our spirit through service. This is a difficult spiritual stage. We cannot leave Shakti Pad without making an adjustment between our ego and our soul. Shakti Pad is unique in that it requires a shift in intention, not just the acquisition of experience or knowledge. Up until now we could do the right things for the wrong reasons and still make spiritual progress. In Shakti Pad we must do the right things for the right reasons. Having the right answer is no longer enough, we must have a pure intention.

If you have been following a role model up to now, this is the time when only your own conscience can guide you. As a student of Yogi Bhajan, I knew when I entered Shakti Pad because all of a sudden he stood back and let me make choices on my own. In Saram Pad and Karam Pad he would use all kinds of encouragement, from love and nurturing to the carrot and stick. His philosophy was simple; he used whatever technique would work.

Yogi Bhajan was asked why he wouldn't correct students who were in Shakti Pad. He gave a cryptic answer without giving away the secret, "I will give that student enough rope to hang themselves." This sounds harsh, but at this stage, it is the student's responsibility to make it or break it. This goes back to my statement about healing, that some things are the teacher's responsibility, some things are the student's responsibility and some things are the Infinite's responsibility. Knowing this is one of the biggest variances between teachers.

The hallmark of Shakti Pad is sacrifice. We continue on the spiritual path not for our own personal gain, but in order to help others more effectively. Our path now becomes a path of purity laid out by our soul. Students in Karam Pad may skip a chance to help someone else in order to do their personal spiritual practice – missing the main point that helping others is the joy of life.

In Shakti Pad we may also begin to think that because we are spiritually accomplished others should start to serve us. This is a test of spiritual ego. We can evaluate our spiritual progress in Shakti Pad by watching how much time our mind spends calculating our personal progress and survival and how much time we spend calculating how to serve and uplift others.

SEVEN STEPS TO HAPPINESS

Commitment will give you character
Character will give you dignity
Dignity will give you divinity (when you have no duality)
Divinity will give you grace
Grace will give you power to sacrifice
Power to sacrifice will give you
Happiness.

– YOGI BHAJAN

During this process, we learn to trust in the Infinite and challenge our ego by refusing to follow the ego's direction. Eventually we learn that the Infinite is indeed the Doer. This state of awareness is called Sahej Pad and hinges on our faith in the Infinite. One of the great advantages of serving a spiritual teacher is observing their faith in the Infinite. I personally observed over and over again how Yogi Bhajan's soul had infinite trust in the Infinite and how he instructed his ego to sit tight and just watch the play of the Creator.

We can see how a spiritual teacher deals with ego by watching what happens when students voice their fears and negativity. Once I heard a longtime student complain to Yogi Bhajan, "You put that inept person in a crucial position. If they don't come through the entire business will fail." He replied that the success or failure of the business was up to God and he was not going to interfere with the spiritual test and growth of the student. Yogi Bhajan's soul was instructing him that this student's spiritual growth was the most important thing at stake and nothing could shake him from this truth. It was a powerful lesson for those running his businesses.

One of the big problems that people have with a spiritual teacher is they fear he will take away their identity. They think, *He is going to destroy my identity and make me serve him. I'm going to become a slave.* Nothing can be taken from us that was given to us by God. If something is taken from us, it is taken by God, and if something is given to us, it was given by God. I didn't always have this belief in terms of my identity.

I found that whatever my teacher could take away from me wasn't God-given; it was created by my ego. What you find when your teacher has worked on you sufficiently is that you are left with nothing but your God-given identity. All he has stripped you of is your ego identity.

Worried, tired and frustrated we seek some way to be happy. In our culture which markets happiness commercially, we receive little more than external stimulation. Unfortunately, we do not understand how to accomplish anything of value by doing nothing. There is an art to being. There is an art to living without action.

We are a go-and-get it nation. Our imagination tells us that if we don't get it, we are a failure. We don't live for ourselves, we live to compete with others. This takes us far from reality. We create our own neurosis when our emotions and desires override our capacity. When we cannot handle our desires and be positive and consistent, we become neurotic. Our mind creates escape routes because we have no spiritual strength to call on.

The most important thing to learn is that we do not have to act. When the mind claims that we have to act and gives us reasons based on fear or vengeance, we know immediately that our ego is talking. We can choose not to act.

We get into so much trouble following the advice of the ego that we will generally come out ahead doing nothing rather than acting according to its advice. We can learn not to listen and act on the ego's instruction. This involves challenging the ego to prove it is right. When the ego instructs you to act out of fear or vengeance, do absolutely nothing. See if things go wrong, stay the same, or get better. If the ego is not quieted, we cannot only not act, we can do the very thing the ego tells us not to do and see if we aren't taken care of by the Infinite.

There is only one false God and that is our ego. Our ego is that entity created by our soul to guarantee our eternal life. The miracle of life is that everything that happens on Earth is for our own benefit. The super miracle of life is that this is true for all souls at all times simultaneously. This earthly existence is quite crude when compared with our conscience. In this human form our soul finds that almost all life on Earth exists by taking the life of some other being. We call this food. The smartest animals are considered to be the predators which exist by eating weaker life forms.

If we agree with this philosophy then humans are the smartest creatures as we are truly the apex predator. The smartest humans then are those who band together to make slaves of every other creature including other humans. The smartest humans then are those that work the least and have the most by taking as much as possible from other life forms. This philosophy is contrary to our conscience and the teachings of every saint that has ever lived. The saints all teach us that actions that are sacrificial are the highest actions. When we serve others without thought of reward we exhibit our highest spiritual nature. The reason that sacrifice has a high spiritual value is that sacrifice is anti-ego. Our ego is worried about our self. When we sacrifice to help someone else, we are acting completely opposite to our ego's self-serving nature.

There is a big difference between sacrifice and co-dependency. In co-dependency one person does something for another person and holds them hostage by expecting a favor in return or some kind of payback. This is not true sacrifice; it is an act of making someone else dependent on you. *If you give me what I want I will love you and if you do not then I will hate you.* This is a co-dependent view of love, and certainly not in line with Yogi Bhajan's definition of love:

Love is a strength. Love is goodness, like Godliness there is no limit to it.
There is no shortage in it, no bargaining...Where there is a love, there is
no question; where there is a question, there is no love.

– YOGI BHAJAN

Genuine healing comes from manifesting your destiny which frees you from karma, the cycle of birth and death. Most people concern themselves with healing only their physical body. Living to your soul's higher purpose is true healing. The physical body is just a shell; your soul is infinite.

I firmly believe that nothing burns karma better than service. If you do yoga just to elevate yourself, your progress will be slow if you don't sacrifice to help others. The only thing that heals is your own purity. Whether you want to be a healer or a teacher, the main thing to do is purify yourself. Let go of your ego and any parts of your self-image which don't reflect your true identity. Serenity comes with being comfortable with the way things are and with what you are 'supposed' to do.

I remember at 16 reading a poem a friend wrote:

> *Above all things,*
>
> *all things...*
>
> *I know*
>
> *what is real,*
>
> *what is me.*
>
> *Nothing else matters.*

I railed at this poem. I loved its truth and simplicity, but what about world hunger, nuclear war, pollution, and overpopulation? Weren't these things more important than knowing one's self? After 30 years of reflection, I can see now that he had found the answer to life at a very young age. Knowing yourself, as all the saints and sages say, is the true purpose of life. It is only then that we can act on the voice of our soul and serve others, becoming Godlike in nature, as God is the ultimate Giver.

Be yourself. Be to BE. Exist to manifest your created self. Slow down, there is nowhere to go. You can run all over this Earth and still some day you will have to leave. You can seek all manner of people to tell you what you want to know, but in the end, you only answer to your own conscience. And the only question you will ask of worth is, *Knowing my truth — did I listen, did I act accordingly?*

Sat Nam

KUNDALINI YOGA BASICS

Kundalini Yoga builds the strength in you. You become you.

– YOGI BHAJAN

KUNDALINI YOGA BASICS

THE YOGA OF AWARENESS

Kundalini Yoga is designed to give an experience of elevation and well-being through raising the flow of energy – the Kundalini – in each of us. Consciousness is biological in nature; it is controlled by the secretion of chemicals in the brain. When the Kundalini rises it activates these chemicals creating significant changes in consciousness. With consistent practice of Kundalini Yoga, your heart opens and change occurs on every level of your life – body, mind and soul.

CREATE A COMFORTABLE ENVIRONMENT

Use a cushioned mat, natural fiber blanket or ideally a sheepskin (to protect you from the Earth's electromagnetic field) and select a quiet place where you will not be interrupted. It is best to do yoga on an empty stomach. When you practice yoga many emotions can arise in the process of transformation. Drinking water will balance you emotionally.

Wear comfortable clothing made of natural fibers – white is recommended as it is psychologically uplifting and expands your aura. It's a good idea to use a shawl during meditation to keep your spine warm and a head covering to strengthen your electromagnetic field and contain the energy that circulates to the brain. Keep your feet bare to conduct the electromagnetic energy through the body's 72,000 nerve endings which end in the feet.

WARM-UPS

The Kundalini Yoga kriyas in this book contain advanced postures. It is important to spend time warming up before beginning these kriyas to increase your flexibility and avoid injury. Recommended warm-ups include: *Spinal Flex, Cat-Cow,* and *Life Nerve Stretch;* pranayam sequences; a few repetitions of the short version of *Sun Salutation;* and any short Kundalini Yoga kriya. If you are a beginner, start with the minimum time given for each posture. Begin slowly and keep a steady rhythm as you increase your pace.

YOGA DURING MENSTRUATION & PREGNANCY

During the heavy days of your menstrual cycle, avoid strenuous yoga like *Stretch Pose, Breath of Fire, Bow Pose, Camel Pose, Locust Pose, Root Lock (Mulbhand), Sat Kriya, Shoulder Stand* or any inverted posture, and *Leg Lifts.*

After the 120th day of pregnancy, or earlier if she has medical complications, a woman should *not* practice the Ten Body Kundalini Yoga sets as they contain many strenuous exercises.

All of the Ten Body meditations are fine for pregnant women as long as it feels comfortable, except the Pranic Body *Meditation for a Stable Self.* A woman should not hold the breath out during pregnancy as this could deprive the fetus of oxygen. Meditations that involve holding the breath in are fine during pregnancy as long as the breath is held in no longer than twenty seconds. This strengthens the diaphragm and helps the woman prepare for birth.

TUNING IN TO START

To prepare for yoga practice, sit in Easy Pose (cross-legged), with your spine straight. Press the hands together in Prayer Pose at the center of the chest, sides of the thumbs pressed against the sternum. With your eyes closed, focus your concentration at the Third Eye point located between the eyebrows at the root of the nose, about a half inch under the skin.

Inhale deeply and as you exhale chant the Adi Mantra, *Ong Namo Guru Dev Namo,* on one breath. The sound *Dev* is chanted a minor third higher than the other sounds. If you cannot chant it all on one breath, then take a short breath after *Ong Namo*

Ong... Namo...   Guru Dev... Namo...

to complete the mantra. Repeat the mantra three times in all. You can hear the Adi Mantra chanted online at www.kriteachings.org in the Students & Teachers section under Kundalini Yoga Mantras.

The meaning of *Ong Namo Guru Dev Namo* is:

> *I call on the creative infinite consciousness of the universe.*

> *I call on the divine wisdom within me.*

YOGIC BREATHING

Pranayam is the science of utilizing the breath for optimal vitality and peace of mind. Since the mind follows the rate of the breath, changing our breathing patterns can create profound changes in our internal universe.

LONG DEEP BREATHING

By taking a deep yogic breath you can expand your lung capacity about eight-fold. As you inhale, your navel and abdomen move outward, then you fill the chest, upper ribs and clavicle. On the exhale release the breath from the top down and pull your navel and abdomen in to push all the breath out. Be sure to exhale completely to empty the lungs, which will facilitate a deeper inhalation.

Long Deep Breathing develops endurance and patience. If you slow your breath to 8 breaths per minute, your pituitary gland secretes fully; if the breath is slowed to 4 breaths per minute the pineal gland is stimulated and deep meditation is automatic.

BREATH OF FIRE

In Breath of Fire your breath is powerful, continuous and rapid, about 2 - 3 breaths per second, and you breathe though the nose only. Breath of Fire is powered from the navel point and solar plexus. As you exhale, the breath is expelled powerfully through the nose by pressing your navel and solar plexus toward the spine. As you inhale the upper abdominal muscles relax and the diaphragm extends down. The breath seems to come in as part of relaxation rather than through effort. There is no pause between the inhale and exhale and equal power is given to both.

Breath of Fire releases toxins and expands your lung capacity, strengthens the navel increasing vitality, and repairs the balance between the sympathetic and parasympathetic nervous systems to increase your resistance to stress.[9]

EYE FOCUS

Unless otherwise instructed, your eyes remain closed and focused between the eyebrows and up about a quarter of an inch at the Third Eye or Brow Point. This stimulates the pituitary gland and allows you to focus on the movements, breath and mantra involved.

MEDITATING ON *SAT NAM*

During Kundalini Yoga mantras are often linked with the breath to enhance their ability to direct the mind through rhythmic repetition. The most common mantra is *Sat Nam,* which is pronounced *Sat Naam,* and means *Truth is my identity.* Unless otherwise instructed mentally repeat *Sat* as you inhale and *Nam* as you exhale while doing Kundalini Yoga postures.

MUDRAS

Kundalini Yoga contains many mudras – specific hand and finger positions – which enable you to guide reflexes to the brain. Each mudra gives a clear message to the mind/body energy system. For example, Gyan Mudra stimulates wisdom and increases receptivity and calmness.

VENUS LOCK

MEN: With the palms facing each other, interlace the fingers with the left little finger on the bottom. Put the left thumb tip just above the base of the thumb on the webbing between the thumb and index finger of the right hand. The tip of the right thumb presses the fleshy mound at the base of the left thumb.

WOMEN: Women reverse the sequence of alternating the fingers so that the right little finger is on the bottom and the tip of the left thumb presses the fleshy mound of the right thumb.

BODY LOCKS

The bandhas are locks which direct the flow of life energy within the body and aura. They consolidate the effects of your efforts enabling you to bring about subtle transformation.

MULBANDH: ROOT LOCK

Mulbandh, or Root Lock, stimulates the flow of spinal fluid. Unless otherwise stated, end each yoga posture with Mulbandh. It can be applied with the breath held in or out. Mulbandh is a smooth rapid motion that consists of three parts: contract the muscles of the sphincter inward and upward; contract the area around the sex organ as if trying to stop the flow of urine; then contract the lower abdominal muscles and navel point toward the spine. Use only the muscles necessary to hold the lock.

JALANDHAR BANDH: NECK LOCK

This lock is generally applied when holding the breath in or out, with Mulbandh, and during chanting meditations. To apply Neck Lock pull the spine straight, lift the chest up and at the same time gently stretch the back of the neck by pulling the chin in to allow the flow of energy through the neck. Do not bring the head down; bring the chest up to increase mobility in your upper back. Keep your face and neck muscles relaxed.

Jalandhar Bandh opens the energy of the medulla oblongata in the brain stem, and allows the energy to flow more effectively to the pineal and pituitary glands in the brain. When the pituitary rotates, the *'cup of nectar'* (the secretion of the pituitary) flows down to the heart and the Kundalini is awakened.[10]

KUNDALINI MUSIC

Music enhances the effects of breathing, mantra and meditation in Kundalini Yoga. Yogi Bhajan specified that we play only 3HO music in Kundalini Yoga classes, because its subtle rhythms create inner energy and elevation.

RELAXATION

It is important to rest between postures unless otherwise instructed, to get the maximum benefit from the kriyas. If you are a beginner and especially if the kriya is strenuous, relax in *Easy Pose* or *Corpse Pose* for 30 seconds to 3 minutes. This allows the energy generated and the glandular secretions released to circulate throughout the body.

Corpse Pose is done lying on your back with your hands by your sides, palms facing up, and your ankles uncrossed, feet relaxed. After the kriya, it is important to relax for 5-10 minutes in *Corpse Pose.* Cover yourself to contain the energy you've created and stay warm. Afterwards, roll your ankles and wrists a few times in each direction, hug your knees and rock on your spine a few times, then sit up. At this time you may choose to continue with a meditation or end your session with the *'Long Time Sun'* song – see Closing Song.

CLOSING SONG

Kundalini yogis traditionally sing the following to end a yoga class:

> *May the long time sun shine upon you,*
> *All love surround you, and the pure light within you,*
> *Guide your way on.*
> *May the long time sun shine upon you,*
> *All love surround you, and the pure light within you,*
> *Guide your way on, guide your way on, guide your way on...*

Then inhale deeply to chant: *Saaaaaaaaaaaaaat Nam* in a ratio of 8:1. You may end with a prayer and/or by bringing your forehead to the floor briefly for a reflective moment.

KUNDALINI YOGA & MEDITATION FOR THE TEN BODIES

Your pranic body and your auric body must coincide to keep you young and alive. That's where youth is.

– YOGI BHAJAN

THE SOUL

1st Body

You have a soul, the spirit by which you live. Your soul is an electromagnetic psyche which puts everything together for you.

— YOGI BHAJAN

THE SOUL BODY KRIYA FOR DIVINITY

Throughout the kriya, concentrate at the Third Eye point with your eyes closed, and do long, deep breathing for 1-3 minutes, unless otherwise specified.

1 Sufi Grind. Sit in Easy Pose with your hands on your knees. Begin circling your torso from the base in one direction, keeping your spine straight. Feel the maximum stretch at the heart level. Inhale as you rotate forward, exhale as you rotate back. Change directions halfway though. To end, inhale, straighten the spine and apply Mulbandh; exhale and relax.

2 Still sitting, stretch your legs straight out. Raise your left leg up to a 60 degree angle, tilting the straight spine to a 60 degree angle. Stretch the arms straight forward parallel to the floor with palms facing each other. Maintain the position, apply a slight Jalandhar Bandh and do Breath of Fire. Then relax your leg down and repeat the posture with the right leg raised.

3   Spinal Twist. Sit in Easy Pose and stretch your arms to the sides. Bend
the elbows and grasp your shoulders with your fingers in front, thumbs
in back. Pull back on the elbows slightly. Inhale and twist the torso left;
exhale and twist right, keeping your upper arms parallel to the ground.
Let your head follow the movement of the chest.

4 Stand with your feet together and raise your left leg. Grab your left ankle with both hands and lift the leg as high as possible balancing on your right foot. Keep your spine and legs straight, shoulders relaxed. Apply a slight Jalandhar Bandh. Concentrate at the Third Eye with your eyes closed or keep them focused at a fixed point to help you balance. Switch legs and repeat.

5 Standing with your feet together, bend forward from the base of your spine, keeping your back straight until it is parallel to the ground. Let your straight arms hang down from your shoulders and move them alternately in a smooth fluid motion. Inhale raising the left arm forward and up and the right arm back and up; exhale as the right arm moves forward and up and the left arm moves backward and up. Both arms should be parallel to the spine at the same time at their maximum reach.

6a   Lie on the floor with your arms extended straight overhead on the floor, palms facing inward.

6b   Inhale and lifting from the chest, sit up and lean forward to touch your toes. Exhale as you return to your back. Keep your arms aligned with the spine throughout the movement.

7a Come onto your hands and knees, spine straight. Your hands are flat on the floor aligned with your shoulders, arms straight. The knees are aligned with the hips. Your head is held so that the neck is parallel with the floor. Raise your left leg up parallel to the ground so it forms a straight line with your spine and neck.

7b Then begin inhaling as you lift your left leg 30 degrees above horizontal, exhaling as you lower it parallel to the floor. Switch legs and repeat.

8   Tree Pose. Stand with your feet together and your hands in Prayer Pose at the Heart Center. Bend your right leg and place your foot on the inside of your left thigh with the heel up and the toes pointing down. Concentrate at the Third Eye with your eyes closed or keep them open and stare at a fixed point on the horizon to help keep your balance. Switch legs and repeat with the left leg.

9 Archer Pose. Stand with the feet together. Rotate the heel of your right foot 90 degrees outward so the toes form a right angle with your left foot. Step directly backwards with the right foot and rotate it 20 degrees inward. With your left foot pointing forward, bend your left knee until your thigh is parallel to the floor and your knee is over the toes. Curl the fingers of both hands into fists with the thumbs pointing up. Bend your right arm and stretch the fist back to your shoulder as you stretch your left arm straight out. Hold the position and focus on your left thumb. Change sides and repeat.

10 Sat Kriya. Sit in Easy Pose and stretch your arms straight up overhead, with the palms together or the fingers interlaced with the index fingers pointing up. Keep the arms straight hugging your ears. As you chant *Sat* pull your navel point in and up; as you chant *Nam* relax the diaphragm and project the sound from the Third Eye. The rhythm is approximately 8 cycles per 10 seconds. As you chant let your breath adjust naturally.

THE SOUL BODY ~ GUIDANCE OF THE SOUL

Time: 11 minutes

Mudra: Sit in Easy Pose with a straight spine. On both hands, touch the tip of the index finger to the tip of the thumb; keep the other fingers straight and spread as wide apart as possible. Secure your elbows firmly into the sides of your ribcage and place your hands in front of each shoulder, palms facing forward. Tilt your forearms forward at a 45 degree angle from the shoulders.

Music: Play the CD *Tantric Har;* if the music is unavailable, move the hands once per second.

Movement: *Remain silent as the music plays.* On each repetition of the mantra *Har* arc the hands from the starting position up and back about 12" and stop them in a dead halt next to the ears, palms still facing forward. Quickly resume the original position and continue, keeping the fingers stiff and separated throughout the movement. Do it powerfully so you are lifted with each upward jerk of the hands.

Eyes: Unspecified.

Comments: This meditation is also known as *Giaan Sudhaa Simran Kriya.* When the exercise becomes painful push through it to reach the stage where there is no pain. Learn to confront and overcome your pain and calamity.

There is something more in Kundalini Yoga than the exercises you do. It is the flow of energy. The fact is that without having your Kundalini awakened, your soul is not awakened.

– YOGI BHAJAN

THE NEGATIVE MIND

2ⁿᵈ Body

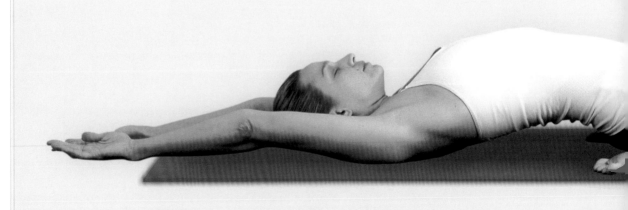

Negative mind is a must, negative mind is given to you for right of life.

– YOGI BHAJAN

THE NEGATIVE MIND KRIYA FOR PROTECTION

Throughout the kriya, concentrate at the Third Eye point with your eyes closed, and do long, deep breathing for 1-3 minutes, unless otherwise specified.

1   Sufi Grind. Sit in Easy Pose with your hands on your knees. Begin circling your torso from the base in one direction, keeping your spine straight. Feel the maximum stretch at the heart level. Inhale as you rotate forward, exhale as you rotate back. Change directions halfway though. To end, inhale, straighten the spine and apply Mulbandh; exhale and relax.

2   Walking Crow. Squat in Crow Pose with the feet flat on the floor and the hands on the knees. Keeping the knees bent and the right foot flat, raise the left heel and move the left knee forward. Then shift your weight, raise the right heel and move the right knee forward. With your eyes open, walk from one knee to the other, exhaling as each knee touches the floor, inhaling as you shift your weight.

3 Lie on your back with your legs straight and your feet together. Pull the shoulders and shoulder blades together under your back and raise your buttocks. The arms remain straight on the floor. Keep the weight evenly distributed on the soles of your feet, your arms and shoulders, neck and head. Hold the posture as you do a powerful Breath of Fire.

4 Cobra Lotus Pose. Sit in Lotus Pose with your right foot on your left thigh, and your left foot on your right thigh. Place your hands by your sides and push up to bring your weight on your knees. Slowly lower yourself onto your stomach with your elbows bent and arch up into Cobra Pose, lifting your head last. Lift your chin without compromising your neck. Keep your shoulders relaxed and pulled slightly down.

If you cannot do the Cobra Lotus Pose, do the variation as pictured above. Start by lying on your stomach with your forehead on the floor. Place your hands under your shoulders pointing forward. Bend your knees, cross your ankles and raise your feet towards your buttocks. Raise the chest and arch slowly into Cobra Pose, lifting your head last. Lift your chin without compromising your neck. Keep your shoulders relaxed and pulled slightly down.

5   Sit in Easy Pose with your hands in Gyan Mudra.

(continued)

Keep your eyes wide open and rotate them in a clockwise direction, keeping your head fixed. Move your eyes precisely with the breath in the fashion described below; change direction to a counter-clockwise rotation half-way though.

Inhale halfway with a short sniff and move your eyes to the upper left corner;

Inhale with a sniff to your maximum capacity, and move your eyes to the upper right corner;

Exhale halfway with a sniff and move your eyes to the lower right corner;

Exhale with a sniff all the breath out and move your eyes to the lower left corner.

6 Lie on your back, pull your knees into your chest and wrap your arms around them. Lift your head and put your nose between your knees. Hold the position and do Breath of Fire.

7 Celibate Pose Stretch. Sit with your buttocks on the floor between the heels. Put your hands behind your back and slowly move back until you are lying flat on the floor with your arms stretched overhead, palms facing up. If this is too difficult, support yourself on the hands or forearms with the spine, head and neck aligned.

8   Triangle Pose. Come onto your hands and knees with your hands shoulder width apart under your shoulders, and the knees hip width apart. Your palms are flat on the floor, fingers spread apart, pointing forward. Roll your toes under so they grip the floor, and lift your buttocks up until your arms and legs are straight with palms and feet flat on the floor, forming a triangle. Press the base of the spine down while lifting the sitting bones upward. Keep the spine, head and neck aligned and apply a slight Jalandhar Bandh. Your eyes are directed toward your navel. Hold the position and inhale in 4 sniffs to maximum; exhale in 1 smooth stroke.

9a Come lying on your stomach with your legs straight, feet together and arms straight overhead, palms together.

9b Inhale and lift your arms, head, upper body and legs into Locust Pose; exhale and come down into the starting position. Continue the motion. To end, inhale and hold the posture briefly; exhale and relax.

THE NEGATIVE MIND ~ WAHE GURU, WAHE JIO PRANAYAM

Time: 31 minutes

Mantra: The mantra is *Wahe Guru, Wahe Guru, Wahe Guru, Wahe Jio. Wahe Guru* is pronounced *Wha-hay Guroo; Jio* is pronounced *Jee-o.*

Mudra: Sit in Easy Pose with the spine straight and your hands in Gyan Mudra. Inhale deeply and on the exhale chant the mantra 8 times aloud on each breath.

Eyes: Close your eyes and concentrate on the Third Eye.

To end: Inhale, hold your breath for a moment, exhale and relax.

Comments: Do this meditation 31 minutes a day for mastery of the Negative Mind.

> *When the mind is backed by the will, the mind is always positive. When it's backed by ego, the mind is always negative. When it is backed by your will, the hand of God will protect you.*
>
> – YOGI BHAJAN

THE POSITIVE MIND

3rd Body

A positive mind tells you what is right in it. It is the conscious mind, it is the gracious mind, it is the noble mind, it is the mind which has grit and courage.

– YOGI BHAJAN

THE POSITIVE MIND KRIYA FOR ACHIEVEMENT

Throughout the kriya, concentrate at the Third Eye point with your eyes closed, and do long, deep breathing for 1-3 minutes, unless otherwise specified.

1   Sufi Grind. Sit in Easy Pose with your hands on your knees. Begin circling your torso from the base in one direction, keeping your spine straight. Feel the maximum stretch at the heart level. Inhale as you rotate forward, exhale as you rotate back. Change directions halfway though. To end, inhale, straighten the spine and apply Mulbandh; exhale and relax.

2a Sit with your legs straight out with your feet together. Keep your spine straight and stretch your arms above your head in line with the spine, palms facing each other. Inhale in this position.

2b Exhale as you bend forward from the base of the spine. Stretch forward with the arms over and beyond the feet without touching them. Inhale up; exhale down in a smooth motion.

3a Sit in Easy Pose with your palms on your knees and apply a slight Jalandhar Bandh. Roll one shoulder forward and the other back, keeping your head and neck straight.

3b Inhale and lift both shoulders; hold briefly, exhale and relax.

4 Sit with the left leg straight out. Bend your right leg and put the sole of your foot against your inner thigh, with your heel against the groin. The right knee touches the floor. Bend your torso forward from the hips.

Hold onto the big toe of your left foot with the left index and middle fingers and press the big toenail with your thumb. Pass your right hand under your left wrist and grasp the outside of your left foot.

With your spine, head and neck straight, apply Mulbandh and Jalandhar Bandh. Keep your eyes open gazing at the big toe of your left foot as you do Breath of Fire. Switch legs and repeat the exercise.

5a   Start in a standing position with your legs shoulder width apart. Raise your arms as high as you can with your fingers interlaced in Venus Lock.

5b   Exhale and squat down into Crow Pose lowering the Venus Lock to the base of your spine. Inhale and stand up as you raise the Venus Lock straight up behind you. Continue the motion.

6a Sit in Easy Pose and place your palms on the knees. Apply a slight Jalandhar Bandh and roll both shoulders in the same direction, keeping your head straight. Switch directions and repeat.

6b Inhale, lift both shoulders and hold a few moments; exhale and relax.

7 Lie on your back with your arms straight alongside your body, palms down. Keeping your feet together, press your back down and raise both legs straight up to 90 degrees. Hold the posture, apply Jalandhar Bandh and do Breath of Fire.

8 Sit in Easy Pose and bring your arms straight out, palms facing each other. Inhale and raise the arms up to 60 degrees, exhale and lower them 60 degrees.

9   Stand with your feet together and raise the arms straight overhead with the palms together. Stretch the spine, lift the ribcage and arch your back. Hold the position as you do Breath of Fire.

10   Lie on your back and lift your arms straight up perpendicular to the floor, parallel to each other with the palms facing. Lift your left leg up to 60 degrees and the right leg 12"; switch legs and continue the motion.

11 Triangle Pose. Come onto your hands and knees with your hands shoulder width apart under your shoulders, and the knees hip width apart. Your palms are flat on the floor, fingers spread apart, pointing forward. Roll your toes under so they grip the floor, and lift your buttocks up until your arms and legs are straight with palms and feet flat on the floor, forming a triangle. Press the base of the spine down while lifting the sitting bones upward. Keep the spine, head and neck aligned and apply a slight Jalandhar Bandh. Your eyes are directed toward your navel. Hold the position and inhale in 4 sniffs to maximum; exhale in 1 smooth stroke.

THE POSITIVE MIND ~ ELIMINATING THOUGHTS YOU DISLIKE

Time: 11 minutes

Mudra: Sit in Easy Pose with the spine straight. Make your hands into a cup with the right hand over the left, fingers crossing each other. Place the cupped hands at the level of the heart center.

Breath: Meditate on the thought you would like to eliminate as you inhale deeply through your nose. Exhale through your mouth, puckering your lips and spitting out the thought into your hands with the breath in a long, slow motion.

Eyes: Look into the cupped hands.

To end: Inhale deeply, exhale, and with your eyes closed, begin to concentrate on all 26 vertebrae from top to bottom. Feel your spine as if you are feeling a stick in your hand; the more you can feel it, the more energy flow and relief will occur.

Comments: You can rewrite your destiny to its highest potential. Yogi Bhajan said, "Destiny is nothing but the outer impression of the inner image a man carries of himself." This meditation can alter your destiny by eliminating persistent negative thoughts from your inner image of yourself so positive thoughts can manifest without interference.

This super-consciousness, the positive mind, shall not rest unless and until you find the Divine in you.

– YOGI BHAJAN

THE NEUTRAL MIND

4th Body

You live by your heart as a human, but it's very difficult to do because you have to have a neutral mind. If you do not have a neutral mind you cannot be consistently constant and know who you are.

– YOGI BHAJAN

THE NEUTRAL MIND KRIYA FOR GUIDANCE

Throughout the kriya, concentrate at the Third Eye point with your eyes closed, and do long, deep breathing for 1-3 minutes, unless otherwise specified.

1   Sufi Grind. Sit in Easy Pose with your hands on your knees. Begin circling your torso from the base in one direction, keeping your spine straight. Feel the maximum stretch at the heart level. Inhale as you rotate forward, exhale as you rotate back. Change directions halfway though. To end, inhale, straighten the spine and apply Mulbandh; exhale and relax.

2 Sit in Easy Pose with the back of the wrists on the knees, arms straight, fingers in Gyan Mudra. Meditate on the breath.

3 Camel ride. Sit on your heels in Rock Pose with the palms on the thighs. Inhale and flex the spine forward lifting and opening the ribcage, exhale and flex the spine back in a smooth motion. Apply a light Mulbandh.

4 Sit on the right ankle with your heel in between the anus and sex organs and your left leg straight out in front of you. With the upper body perpendicular to the floor, raise the right arm straight up and forward parallel to the floor. Raise the left arm straight back parallel to the floor. Both palms face the ceiling. Hold the posture and do Breath of Fire. To end, inhale and hold briefly; exhale and relax.

5a Sit in Easy Pose and raise both arms straight out, palms facing inside parallel to each other and the floor. Raise the left arm up to 60 degrees.

5c Continue the motion with Breath of Fire through a rounded mouth.

5b Begin scissoring the arms, lowering the left arm to the parallel position while raising the right arm to 60 degrees and switching arms.

6 Stand and bring your arms out to the sides parallel to the floor, palms facing forward. Open the legs wide apart with the toes pointing outward and the big toes positioned directly under the wrists. Bend the knees until the thighs are parallel to the floor.

7a Lie on your stomach with straight legs, feet together, top of feet on the floor. Put the palms on the floor under your shoulders. Inhale into Cobra Pose as high as you can comfortably, raising the ribcage and pulling the navel in and up, leaving your hips on the floor.

7b Exhale and slowly move into Baby Pose, sitting back on the heels with your forehead on the floor, your arms straight out parallel to each other on the floor, palms down. Continue moving back and forth between the 2 postures. To end inhale in Cobra, hold briefly, exhale and relax.

8a Sit with the legs straight out in front. Raise the left leg straight and grab the left foot with both hands.

8b Hold the position and inhale, raising the right leg up to the level of the left, exhale lowering it to the floor. Continue this movement. Switch legs and repeat.

9

Standing, raise the arms straight overhead and join the palms together. Inhale and lift the ribcage, arching the spine up and back.

Exhale and bend forward from the hips all the way down and let the arms swing back behind your legs. Continue this movement.

THE NEUTRAL MIND ~ SHABD KRIYA

Time: 15-62 minutes

Mantra: *Sa-Ta-Na-Ma* and *Wahe Guru. Wahe Guru* is pronounced *Wha-hay Guroo.*

Mudra: Sit in a comfortable posture with the spine straight. Place your hands in your lap, right hand over left, palms up with the thumb tips touching and pointing forward.

Breath: Inhale in four equal parts as you mentally vibrate the mantra *Sa-Ta-Na-Ma.* Hold the breath in and vibrate the mantra four times – *Sa-Ta-Na-Ma, Sa-Ta-Na-Ma, Sa-Ta-Na-Ma, Sa-Ta-Na-Ma.* Exhale in two equal strokes as you mentally project *Wahe Guru.*

Eyes: Your eyes focus on the tip of the nose with your eyelids half closed.

Comments: The best time to practice Shabd Kriya is before bed. If practiced regularly, your sleep will be deep and relaxed and your nerves will be regenerated. After a few months of practice your breath will be subconsciously regulated in this rhythm as you sleep! Eventually you will automatically hear the mantra during your daily activities and take on this breath rhythm. You will think better, work better, share better, love better and fight better.

Mystically the effect is understood through Numerology. The number 11 is the number of Infinity in the material world, and conqueror of the physical realm. The number 22 is the infinite number of longing and gives mastery of the mental realm. Shabd Kriya regulates the breath in 22 beats which gives your mind the power to stretch to the Infinite. It gives radiance and patience which makes your personality universal.

Service creates a permanent love and friendship. Self-discipline creates grace. And a neutral mind creates wisdom. These are the rules of life.

– YOGI BHAJAN

THE PHYSICAL BODY

5th Body

*The process of self-healing is the privilege of every being.
Self-healing is not a miracle. Self-healing is the genuine
process of relationship between the physical and the
infinite power of the soul.*

– YOGI BHAJAN

THE PHYSICAL BODY KRIYA FOR SELF-HEALING

Throughout the kriya, concentrate at the Third Eye point with your eyes closed, and do long, deep breathing for 1-3 minutes, unless otherwise specified.

1   Sit in Rock Pose with your hands on your thighs and apply a light Mulbandh. Inhale and flex your spine forward, lifting and opening the ribcage. Exhale and flex back in a smooth motion.

2   Sufi Grind. Sit in Easy Pose with your hands on your knees. Begin circling your torso from the base, keeping your spine straight. Feel the maximum stretch at the heart level. Inhale as you rotate forward, exhale as you rotate back. Change directions halfway though. To end, inhale, straighten the spine and apply Mulbandh; exhale and relax.

3 Sit in Rock Pose with your spine straight. Stretch your arms overhead parallel to each other with the palms facing in. Exhale and bend from the hips until your body, head and arms are parallel to the floor. Inhale and rise up with your upper body, head and arms in a straight line. Keep your buttocks in contact with the heels. Continue this motion.

4   Lie on your back with your arms at your sides and press your back down as you lift both legs straight up to 45 degrees. Inhale and open the legs wide apart; exhale and close the legs. Continue this motion.

5a Stand up with your legs shoulder width apart. The arms are straight out parallel to each other and the floor, palms facing in.

5b Exhale through the nose and squat down into Crow Pose keeping the arms straight out in front of you. Inhale through rounded lips and return to the standing position. Continue this motion.

6   Stand with your hands in Prayer Pose at the center of your chest. Exhale and take a big step back with the left leg, stretching your arms overhead, palms still together. Lift your chest and balance on your right foot and the toes of your left foot, with your right thigh parallel to the floor. Inhale and step back to the starting position lowering the mudra. Continue the movement alternating legs with the breath.

7 From a standing position as you exhale bend forward from the hips grasping the back of the right thigh with both hands. Raise the left leg back and up parallel to the floor. Keep the upper body close to the right thigh and hold the position. Switch legs and repeat.

8 Sit with your legs straight out in front. Bring your arms straight up parallel to the floor and to each other, palms facing in. Raise the left leg up 60 degrees and lean back just enough to balance yourself. Hold the position and do Breath of Fire. Do not switch legs; the posture is done on one side only.

9 Stretch Pose. Lie on your back and bring your feet together. Keeping your arms straight, raise your hands next to or over your thighs without touching your body. Press your lower back down as you raise your legs 6" from the floor, toes pointing forward. Lift your head and shoulders high enough to focus on the toes. Do Breath of Fire.

THE PHYSICAL BODY ~ MEDITATION
FOR PROJECTION & PROTECTION

Time: Start with 11 minutes. Add 5 minutes a day up to 31 minutes, until you perfect it.

Mantra & Movement: Sit in Easy Pose with a straight spine and apply a light Jalandhar Bandh. Place the palms together at the Heart Center in Prayer Pose with the thumbs crossed. Project the mind out as you chant out loud. Time the full extension of the arms to the mantra:

> – Chant *Aad Guray Nameh* as you extend your hands up and out 60 degrees, palms together;
> – Chant *Jugaad Guray Nameh* as you bring the hands back to the starting position;
> – Chant *Sat Guray Nameh* as you extend the arms up and out again;
> – Chant *Siree Guroo Dayvay Nameh* as you return to the starting position.

Meaning:

> *I bow to the Primal Wisdom;*
> *I bow to the Wisdom through the Ages;*
> *I bow to the True Wisdom;*
> *I bow to the great unseen Wisdom.*

Eyes: Unspecified

Comments: This meditation gives you an enchanting, magnetic personality and attracts many friends. It surrounds the magnetic field with protective light.

We have to know our ten bodies. We have to be aware of them all the time. That's how the physical body has to be trained.

– YOGI BHAJAN

THE ARCLINE

6th Body

The arc body and the eyes must connect for someone to feel that you want to communicate. That is where a relationship is created – psyche to psyche.

– YOGI BHAJAN

THE ARCLINE BODY KRIYA FOR ALERTNESS

Throughout the kriya, concentrate at the Third Eye point with your eyes closed, and do long, deep breathing for 1-3 minutes, unless otherwise specified.

1   Sit in Easy Pose and raise your arms parallel to each other and the floor, palms facing each other. Hold the posture.

2   Lock the hands in Bear Grip, right palm facing in, left facing out, and curl the fingers of both hands to form a fist at the level of the heart center. Keep your forearms parallel to the floor and apply Mulbandh. Hold the posture.

3 Sit with your legs straight out, feet together and flexed. Bend forward with your arms in line with your spine, parallel to each other with the palms facing. Stretch over and beyond your feet without touching them and do Breath of Fire.

4 Lie on your back with your feet together and make your hands into fists by the sides of your ribcage. Balancing your weight on your elbows and the soles of your feet, lift your head and body up. Apply Mulbandh and do Breath of Fire.

5a Camel Pose. Sit on your heels in Rock Pose and hold your ankles;

5b Inhale and arch your body up until your thighs are perpendicular to the floor;

5c Let your head drop back, keeping your arms straight. Exhale and lower yourself back into the starting position, bringing your head up after you are sitting in Rock Pose again.

6a Come lying on your stomach with your legs straight out, feet together and arms straight overhead, palms together.

6b Inhale and lift your arms, head, upper body and legs into Locust Pose; exhale and come down into the starting position. Continue this motion. Inhale and hold the posture briefly; exhale and relax.

7   Stand up with your feet together and your hands on your heart center, right over left. Inhale through the nose and round your mouth as you exhale through your lips.

8 Start in Rock Pose. Then come onto your knees and bring your right leg straight forward, keeping the left thigh perpendicular to the floor. Bend the upper body from the hips until your hands reach the floor on each side of the right foot. Hold the posture; then switch legs and repeat.

THE ARCLINE ~ MEDITATION TO CLEAR KARMA FROM THE ARCLINE

Time: 31 minutes

Mantra: The mantra is *Wahe Guru, Wahe Guru, Wahe Guru, Wahe Jio. Wahe Guru* is pronounced *Wha-hay Guroo; Jio* is pronounced *Jee-o.*

Mudra: Sit in Easy Pose with a straight spine. Relax the elbows by your sides and bring your forearms straight out a few inches above the knees, palms slightly cupped, facing up.

Movement: On each repetition of *Wahe Guru* and *Wahe Jio,* scoop your hands up and over the shoulders as far back as you can and return to the starting position. Imagine you are scooping water and throwing it over your arcline with a flick of the wrists. The movement is smooth and follows the rhythm of the music.

Eyes: Closed.

Music: *Wahe Guru, Wahe Guru, Wahe Guru, Wahe Jio* by Gyani Ji.

To end: Inhale and stretch your hands as far as possible behind your head; hold 10-15 seconds, and then exhale. Repeat two more times. Relax.

Comments: This meditation clears your karma from your arcline and allows you to experience what *Wahe Guru* (the ecstasy of God consciousness) really means.

The power of Infinity is not outside of you, it is inside of you. When "I" and Infinity create impact, you'll become totally divine; otherwise there's a duality which keeps you away from reality.

– YOGI BHAJAN

THE AURA

7ᵗʰ Body

*Do you know when you chant 'Sat Nam' with Sat Kriya
you project your aura in absolute and radiation form and
your radiant body becomes twelve inches wide?*

– YOGI BHAJAN

THE AURIC BODY KRIYA FOR SENSITIVITY

Throughout the kriya, concentrate at the Third Eye point with your eyes closed, and do long, deep breathing for 1-3 minutes, unless otherwise specified.

1 Sufi Grind. Sit in Easy Pose with your hands on your knees. Begin circling your torso from the base in one direction, keeping your spine straight. Feel the maximum stretch at the heart level. Inhale as you rotate forward, exhale as you rotate back. Change directions halfway though. To end, inhale, straighten the spine and apply Mulbandh; exhale and relax.

2   Sit with your legs straight out, feet together and flexed. Bend forward with your arms in line with your spine, parallel to each other with the palms facing each other. Stretch over and beyond your feet without touching them and do Breath of Fire.

3   Sit in Easy Pose and raise your arms up to a 60 degree angle. Bend the fingers so your fingertips touch the pads of the palms. The thumbs point straight up, palms face forward. Apply Jalandhar Bandh and do Breath of Fire. To end, inhale and apply Mulbandh, exhale and relax.

4   Stand with your feet together. Bend forward from the hips and place your palms flat on the floor, arms straight. Hold the posture. To end, slowly come standing up.

5   Stand and bring the legs wide apart. Bend your knees until the thighs are parallel to the floor. Balance with your hands on your thighs just above the knees, fingers in front.

6 Standing, bend the right leg and put the outer heel of your foot in your groin so the sole of your foot faces upward. Bend forward from the hips until you reach the floor with the palms of your hands. Let your head relax down and hold the posture. Switch legs and repeat.

7 Sit in Easy Pose with your hands in Prayer Pose. Meditate on the breath.

8   Cobra Pose. Lie on your stomach with your legs straight out, feet together, top of feet on the floor. Put the palms on the floor under your shoulders. Inhale into Cobra Pose as high as you can comfortably, raising the ribcage and pulling the navel in and up, leaving your hips on the floor.

Hold the posture with Sitali breathing — inhale through the open mouth and curled tongue, exhale through the nose.

9 Lie on your back with your arms at your sides, palms on the floor. Apply
Jalandhar Bandh and raise both legs to 60 degrees. Bicycle the legs as
you do Breath of Fire.

THE AURIC BODY ~ GRACE OF GOD MEDITATION

Timing: Practice on an empty stomach twice a day for 40 days.

Mantra: For women: *I am Grace of God*; for men: *I am in the Grace of God.*

Part I: Relax on your back with your eyes closed. Inhale deeply, hold the breath in and silently repeat the mantra ten times; exhale completely, hold the breath out and silently repeat the mantra ten times. Repeat five times for a total of 100 repetitions.

Part II: Relax your breath and with your eyes still closed, slowly come into Easy Pose. Put your right hand in Gyan Mudra on your knee. Raise your left hand as if taking an oath, palm facing forward. Starting with the pinky, tense one finger at a time as you meditate on its governing energy (see below) and repeat the mantra aloud five times. Keep the other fingers straight and relaxed. Repeat with each finger, ending with the thumb, then relax and meditate silently for a few minutes.

FINGER	GOVERNING PLANET	ELEMENT	ASPECTS INFLUENCED
Pinky finger	Mercury	Water	power to relate and communicate; subconscious communication with the self
Ring finger	Sun & Venus	Fire	physical health, vitality, grace and beauty
Middle finger	Saturn	Air	channel emotion to devotion and patience
Index finger	Jupiter	Ether	wisdom & expansion, ability to change
Thumb	none	Earth	positive ego

Comments: If a woman practices this for a year her aura will become tipped with gold or silver. This meditation balances the five elements and is designed to evoke a woman's inner grace, strength and radiance. The power of the affirmation affects a woman's thoughts, behavior and personality and develops physical health, patience and healing ability. It enables women to channel their emotions positively, drop their weaknesses and develop effective communication. It is recommended that during menopause women do the Grace of God meditation five times a day.

This intuitive capacity is natural. The real action behind it is that you become sensitive to the auric radiance of the other person. That radiance comes from the subtle bodies that compose the unseen human structure. All you have to do is compute the signal of the aura as it comes to you.

– Yogi Bhajan

THE AURIC BODY ~ KIRTAN KRIYA

Sit in Easy Pose with your elbows straight, hands in Gyan Mudra to start.

Mudra: The mudra changes as the fingertips of each hand touch in turn the tip of the thumbs with firm pressure. Each time the fingers press the thumbs the mudra seals the effect of that particular mudra in your consciousness. Each repetition of the mantra takes 3-4 seconds:

On *Saa* press the first or Jupiter fingers to the thumb tips in Gyan Mudra to activate knowledge;

On *Taa* press the second or Saturn fingers to the thumb tips in Shuni Mudra to activate wisdom and patience;

On *Naa* press the third or Sun fingers to the thumb tips in Surya Mudra to activate vitality;

On *Maa* press the fourth or Mercury fingers to the thumb tips in Buddhi Mudra to activate the ability to communicate.

As you move the fingers, keep the elbows straight and chant the mantra in the three languages of consciousness: the voice of humans, lovers and the Divine. The human voice represents the world – chant aloud; the voice of lovers represents our longing to belong – chant in a loud whisper; and the voice of the Divine represents Infinity – chant silently.

Mantra: The primal sounds of Kirtan Kriya, *Sa-Ta-Na-Ma,* represent the cycle of creation. From the Infinite comes life and individual existence; from life comes death or change; from death comes the rebirth of consciousness to the joy of the Infinite which leads back to life.

> *Sa:* Infinity, cosmos, beginning
>
> *Ta:* Life, existence
>
> *Na:* Death, change, transformation
>
> *Ma:* Rebirth

Time: Begin the meditation by chanting aloud for 5 minutes, then whisper for 5 minutes, then go deeply into the sound vibrating the mantra silently for 10 minutes. Come back to a whisper again for 5 minutes and then chant aloud for 5 minutes. The last minute of the 31 minutes is a time for silent prayer.

Eyes: To circulate the prana or cosmic energy properly, meditate in an 'L' form. Imagine the energy of each sound moving down through the Crown Chakra, the solar center at the top of the head, and out through the Third Eye point as it is projected to Infinity. This is the pathway of the Golden Cord – the connection between the pineal and pituitary glands.

To end: End the meditation by inhaling and exhaling deeply several times, stretching your spine up with your hands overhead, fingers spread wide.

Comments: This meditation brings a total mental balance to the individual psyche. Vibrating on the fingertips alternates the electrical polarities. The index and ring fingers are electrically negative relative to the other fingers. This balances the electromagnetic projection of the aura. The duration of Kirtan Kriya may vary as long as the proportion of chanting aloud, in a whisper, and silently, is maintained.

The simplest meditation is Sa-Ta-Na-Ma. It is a sound current. There are three things man has not developed which he must develop in meditation – the frontal lobe, the thalamus and the hypothalamus. When they are undeveloped there is no difference between man and animal…In this meditation we put our physical body with our mental strength to penetrate and awaken our spirit. It's a very simple sound, Sa-Ta-Na-Ma, but if you do it for 31 minutes, it will put your potentials together into unisonness.

– YOGI BHAJAN

THE PRANIC BODY

8th Body

If the pranic body is weak you won't be jubilant even with every environment in your favor.

– YOGI BHAJAN

THE PRANIC BODY KRIYA FOR VITALITY

Throughout the kriya, concentrate at the Third Eye point with your eyes closed, and do long, deep breathing for 1-3 minutes, unless otherwise specified.

1 Sit in Easy Pose and bring your arms out to the side parallel to the floor, palms facing forward. Move your torso from side to side, inhaling to the left, exhaling to the right, keeping the arms parallel to the floor.

2 Sit in Easy Pose with your hands on your knees and begin neck rolls. Inhale while your head rolls backwards, exhale as you roll your head forward in a complete circle. Continue the motion.

3   Sit with your legs straight out, feet together. Bend the upper body forward from the base, keeping the spine straight. The arms are parallel, palms facing each other. Stretch over and beyond your feet without touching them, hold, and do Breath of Fire.

4   Spinal Flex. Sit in Easy Pose and hold your ankles. Apply a light Mulbandh and inhale as you flex your spine forward, lifting and opening the ribcage. Exhale as you flex back, rounding the spine. Continue with a smooth motion.

5   Lie on your stomach and raise yourself up onto your elbows, forearms and feet. The elbows are not as wide as the shoulders and the hands are in Prayer Pose with the outer edge of your hands on the floor. Your legs, upper body and head remain in a straight line as you hold the posture and do Breath of Fire.

6   Lie on your back with your legs straight, feet together. Bring your arms over your head on the floor with the palms facing the ceiling, and do Breath of Fire. To end, inhale and stretch, exhale and relax.

7 Sit in Easy Pose with your hands in Prayer Pose, and then separate the hands a little keeping only the index fingers together along their entire length. Press the index fingers to hold them together.

8 Sit with your legs straight out, feet together. Put the hands behind you keeping the elbows straight. Lift your legs until they reach 60 degrees, hold, and do Breath of Fire.

9 Sit in Easy Pose with your hands in Prayer Pose at the center of the chest. Meditate on the breath.

10a Stand and raise your arms overhead, palms together, and inhale as you lift the ribcage and arch the spine up and back;

10b Exhale and bend forward from the hips until the hands reach the floor and the body is in Triangle Pose, palms flat on the floor, head down;

10c Inhale and sit back in Baby Pose with your arms straight out, forehead and palms on the floor.

From Baby Pose reverse the order: exhale back into Triangle; inhale, stand and lean back. Continue moving from posture to posture in this rhythm: a, b, c, b, a, etc.

THE PRANIC BODY ~ MEDITATION
FOR A STABLE SELF

Time: 3-11 minutes. 11 minutes is the maximum time to practice this kriya.

Mudra: Sit in Easy Pose with the spine straight and apply a light Jalandhar Bandh. Hold this mudra 4-6" in front of the body and make fists with the thumbs pointing straight up. Hold the right hand in front of your throat with the tip of your thumb at mouth level and the left thumb tip about 2" below the right hand. The thumbs should be aligned with one another. Hold the elbows so that the forearms are parallel to the ground and keep the thumbs stiff and in perfect position throughout.

Breath: Regulate the breath by inhaling deeply and quickly; then immediately exhale powerfully and completely. Lock the breath out with the chest suspended. Count to 26 as you visualize energy and awareness moving up the spine, vertebra by vertebra. On each count gently apply Mulbhand and feel the Navel Point squeeze backward.

Eyes: The eyelids are 1/10th open, eyes focused at the Brow Point.

Comments: This is an advanced meditation. Holding the posture precisely is very demanding, and you must concentrate and visualize the energy flow perfectly. It gives complete stability of the Pranic Body which enhances the sense of self, increases good judgment and eliminates conscious and subconscious fears.

The purpose of giving you the prana, the breath of life, was so that you could use each prana innocently to be pure.

– YOGI BHAJAN

THE SUBTLE BODY

9th Body

If a person is very acknowledging and has all essences in harmony, then he can use his subtle body. And the subtle beam is so powerful that it can move the unmovable just by thought.

— YOGI BHAJAN

THE SUBTLE BODY KRIYA FOR REFINEMENT

Throughout the kriya, concentrate at the Third Eye point with your eyes closed, and do long, deep breathing for 1-3 minutes, unless otherwise specified.

1   Sufi Grind. Sit in Easy Pose with your hands on your knees. Begin circling your torso from the base in one direction, keeping your spine straight. Feel the maximum stretch at the heart level. Inhale as you rotate forward, exhale as you rotate back. Change directions halfway though. To end, inhale, straighten the spine and apply Mulbandh; exhale and relax.

2 Sit in Easy Pose and bring your arms up with your elbows bent. Keep the upper arms parallel to the floor and the forearms perpendicular to the floor. Bend the wrists so that your palms are flat facing upward, fingers pointing out.

3 Cat-Cow Pose. Come onto your hands and knees with your arms parallel to each other and the thighs, hands under your shoulders and knees under your hips. Inhale and arch your spine into Cow Pose, exhale and round the spine into Cat Pose. Let your spine flex first and your head follow. Continue this motion.

4 Standing, take a big step back with your left leg and grip the floor with your toes. Bend your right knee until your thigh is parallel to the floor and your foot is flat under your knee. Raise your left arm in front of you and your right arm behind you, parallel to the floor with the palms facing upward. Switch legs.

5 Lie on your back with your feet together and make your hands into fists by the sides of your ribcage. Balancing your weight on your elbows and the soles of your feet, lift your head and body up. Apply Mulbandh and do Breath of Fire.

6 Standing, bend forward from the hips and put the palms of your hands under the soles of your feet with the back of your hands on the floor.

7   Bow Pose. Lie on your stomach, bend your knees and reach back to grab your ankles. Use the thigh muscles to pull the upper body off the ground, then lift the legs. As the chest raises, let the neck and head follow. Hold the position and do Breath of Fire.

8   Sit with your legs straight out. Lean back a bit for balance as you raise your legs up to 60 degrees. Your arms are parallel to each other and the floor, palms facing in, fingers pointing forward. Hold the position and do Breath of Fire.

9   Sit in Easy Pose or Lotus Pose and place your hands on the floor near your knees. Put the weight of your body on your hands, arms and shoulders, and lift your body from the floor. Hold the posture.

10   Stretch Pose variation. Lie on your back and bring your feet together. Keeping your arms straight, raise your hands next to or over your thighs without touching your body. Press your lower back down as you raise your legs 12" from the floor, toes pointing forward. Lift your head and shoulders high enough to focus on the toes. Do Breath of Fire. *In this variation of Stretch Pose the legs are 6" higher than normal.*

THE SUBTLE BODY ~ WAHE GURU MEDITATION

Time: 11-31 minutes

Mudra: Sit in a meditative posture with the spine straight and your hands in Gyan Mudra.

Mantra: The mantra is *Wahe Guru*, pronounced *Wha-hay Guroo*.

Movement: Turn your head to the left, bringing your chin over your shoulder as you chant *Wahe*, then turn your head to the right and bring your head over your shoulder as you chant *Guru*. Focus on the union of the lower and higher triangles formed by the tip of the nose and the eyes, and the eyes and Third Eye point.

Whatever you say, you must be in a position to hear. If you cannot hear what you speak, you will never hear the subtle voice of your own consciousness speaking to you.

— YOGI BHAJAN

THE RADIANT BODY

10th Body

As much you say to me you love me, if you just say to yourself you love yourself, you know what will happen? I will be around you all the time because your radiant body will be so radiant.

— YOGI BHAJAN

THE RADIANT BODY KRIYA FOR COURAGE

Throughout the kriya, concentrate at the Third Eye point with your eyes closed, and do long, deep breathing for 1-3 minutes, unless otherwise specified.

1 Sit in Easy Pose and bring your arms up with your elbows bent. Keep the upper arms parallel to the floor and the forearms perpendicular to the floor. Bend the wrists so that your palms are flat facing upwards, fingers pointing out.

2 Sit in Easy Pose with your hands in Prayer Pose at the center of your chest.

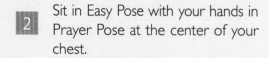

3 Sufi Grind. Sit in Easy Pose with your hands on your knees. Begin circling your torso from the base in one direction, keeping your spine straight. Feel the maximum stretch at the heart level. Inhale as you rotate forward, exhale as you rotate back. Change directions halfway though. To end, inhale, straighten the spine and apply Mulbandh; exhale and relax.

4 Come onto your hands and knees. Lift the left leg until you can grab your left ankle with your right hand. Pulling with the left leg let the right arm act as a lever to stretch the shoulder and open the chest. Holding the position do Breath of Fire. Switch legs and repeat with opposite arms and legs.

5a Bridge Pose. Sit with your legs bent and your feet flat on the floor shoulder width apart. Place your hands on the floor behind you.

5b Inhale and raise your hips until they are in a straight line with the upper body and thighs. Exhale and lower the hips down to the original position. Continue the motion. Keep your chin parallel to the floor in both positions.

6 Stand and bend forward from the hips with your palms together reaching forward. At the same time, raise the right leg straight back. Keep the upper body, head and arms in a straight line parallel to the floor. Hold this posture.

7   Stand with your legs shoulder width apart. Inhale and squat down into Crow Pose while raising the arms overhead with the palms together. Exhale and stand up, lowering the arms to your sides. Continue this motion.

8   Lie on your back and raise your legs straight up to 90 degrees, feet together and flexed so the soles face the ceiling. Raise your arms up to 90 degrees with the palms facing each other. Hold this posture.

THE RADIANT BODY ~
GURU GOBIND SINGH
SHAKTI MANTRA MEDITATION

Time: 11- 31 minutes.

Mudra: Sit in Easy Pose with the elbows straight and the hands in Gyan Mudra.

Eyes: Closed, concentrating at the Third Eye.

Mantra: The mantra is chanted in a monotone: *Wahe Guru, Wahe Guru, Wa-he Wa-he Wa-he Guru. Wahe Guru* is pronounced *Wha-hay Guroo.* Chant two complete cycles of the mantra with each breath, then take a deep rapid breath and continue.

Rhythm:
     Wha -1 beat, *hay* -1 beat, *Gu* - 1/2 beat, *roo* -1 beat, 1/2 beat pause;
     Wha -1 beat, *hay* -1 beat, *Gu* - 1/2 beat, *roo* -1 beat, 1/2 beat pause;
     Wha -1 beat, *hay*- 1 beat, *Wha* - 1 beat, *hay* -1 beat;
     Wha -1 beat, *hay* -1 beat, *Gu* -1/2 beat, *roo* -1 beat, 1/2 beat pause.

To end: Inhale and concentrate at the top of the head, exhale and relax.

Comments: This is the science of Laya Yoga which combines breath, rhythm and mantra to produce an altered state of consciousness, a state of ecstasy. Each repetition of the mantra creates psychic heat. When you rotate the breath and volume of sound properly the heat created burns off your karma. This kriya also calms the nerves and can help reduce fever.

You are wrong if you think your intelligence works or your words are powerful or you are very charismatic. Actually it is your radiant body, the glow, the shine in you that works.

– YOGI BHAJAN

YOGI BHAJAN (1929-2004)

Yogi Bhajan, Ph.D., was both Master of Kundalini Yoga and Mahan Tantric of White Tantric Yoga. He came to the West and reached out to young people who were experimenting with drugs. Recognizing their deep desire to experience higher consciousness, in 1969 he founded 3HO Foundation, the Healthy, Happy, Holy Organization. A drug rehabilitation program, 3HO SuperHealth, opened its doors in 1973 and successfully utilized Kundalini Yoga to empower people by giving them control over their minds, emotions, and actions.

Yogi Bhajan inspired and counseled people for over 34 years with wisdom, humor, and compassion. He gave over 8,000 recorded lectures around the globe, and authored many books to carry his teachings forward into the Aquarian Age. Today Kundalini Yoga classes are offered worldwide in 38 countries. You can still practice White Tantric Yoga with Yogi Bhajan via his subtle body on recorded videos, to take advantage of this super technology to cleanse the subconscious.

Yogi Bhajan is one of only four humanitarians to receive a *Joint Congressional Resolution* from the United States Congress honoring his life's work and teachings. The other recipients are Martin Luther King, Mother Teresa and Pope John Paul II.

Yogi Bhajan, known affectionately as Yogiji to hundreds of thousands worldwide, left his physical body on October 6th, 2004. His mission "to create teachers, not collect students" will be well served by the thousands of Kundalini Yoga teachers who follow in his footsteps, making it their mission to share the art and science of *Kundalini Yoga as Taught by Yogi Bhajan*™.

ABOUT THE AUTHOR

Siri Atma Singh Khalsa, M.D., is an engaging speaker in the field of yoga, healing and medicine. He travels internationally to offer workshops on the healing essence of Kundalini Yoga, the nature of the soul, and loving relationships. Dr. Siri Atma also does personal Yogic Consultations while on tour and year-round by telephone.

Dr. Siri Atma is an Internist and holds an undergraduate degree in Philosophy & Religion. He was trained by Yogi Bhajan and blessed to serve as his personal physician for eight years. Yogi Bhajan called him a *medical intuitive* and a *pure healer,* which aptly describe his ability to tune into what people need at a deep level in order to heal.

CDs and DVDs of Dr. Siri Atma's lectures serve as valuable companions to the material presented in *Waves of Healing. The Yoga, Healing & Medicine* series includes:

· *The Healing Potential of Morning Sadhana*
· *Listening to the Voice of Your Soul*
· *The Medical Basis of Kundalini Yoga*
· *Self Sensory Healing*
· *Merging Your Soul with the Infinite*

For more information contact Dr. Siri Atma via his website, **www.DrSiriAtma.com.**

RESOURCES FOR FURTHER GROWTH

Siri Atma Singh Khalsa, M.D.
To schedule a Yogic Consultation by phone with the author or order CDs or DVDs of his workshop lectures, please visit: **www.DrSiriAtma.com.**

Related Books
Yogi Bhajan, *The Teachings of Yogi Bhajan: The Power of the Spoken Word*
Yogi Bhajan, *The Aquarian Teacher: KRI Level 1 Textbook & Yoga Manual*
Yogi Bhajan, *Praana Praanee Praanayam: Exploring Breath Technology*
Shakti Parwha Kaur Khalsa, *Kundalini Yoga: The Flow of Eternal Power*
Mukta Kaur Khalsa, *Meditations for Addictive Behavior*

Yogi Bhajan Every Day Quotes
www.aquarianwisdom.com – Desk Calendars
ybquotes.aquarianwisdom.org – Email format available in six languages

3HO   For a Kundalini Yoga teacher contact IKYTA: www.kundaliniyoga.com
For Summer & Winter Solstice: www.3ho.org
For White Tantric Yoga: www.whitetantricyoga.com

KRI   For Teacher Training Certification, books, DVDs: www.kriteachings.org

Ancient Healing Ways   For Kundalini Yoga music & more: www.a-healing.com

REFERENCES

Yogi Bhajan Quotes
Special thanks to *Aquarian Wisdom Daily Inspirational Calendar,* compiled by Darshan Kaur Khalsa and Satya Kaur Khalsa

Yogi Bhajan Photo Page, Yogi Bhajan Lecture, 3-27-79
Page 12, *Aquarian Wisdom Daily Inspirational Calendar,* 11-17-06
Page 23, *Aquarian Wisdom Daily Inspirational Calendar,* 1-24-86
Page 24, *Aquarian Wisdom Daily Inspirational Calendar,* 11-16-06, Yogi Bhajan Lecture, 1-24-86
Page 25, Yogi Bhajan Lecture, 12-10-71
Page 27, 28, Yogi Bhajan Lecture, 6-3-90
Page 36, Yogi Bhajan Lecture, 9-11-02
Page 38, Yogi Bhajan Lecture, 7-29-96
Page 39, Yogi Bhajan Lecture, 4-5-00
Page 45, *Aquarian Wisdom Daily Inspirational Calendar,* 12-1-06
Page 45, Yogi Bhajan Lecture, 3-19-85
Page 51, *Aquarian Wisdom Daily Inspirational Calendar,* 12-26-08
Page 54, Yogi Bhajan Lecture, 1-28-80

Page 63, *Aquarian Wisdom Daily Inspirational Calendar,* 7-30-04
Page 67, *Aquarian Wisdom Daily Inspirational Calendar,* 8-16-08, Yogi Bhajan Lecture, 3-27-79
Page 70, *Aquarian Wisdom Daily Inspirational Calendar,* 11-13-06
Page 71, *Aquarian Wisdom Daily Inspirational Calendar,* 7-19-06
Page 77, Yogi Bhajan Lecture, 11-17-89
Page 78, Aquarian *Wisdom Daily Inspirational Calendar,* 8-15-96
Page 79, *Aquarian Wisdom Daily Inspirational Calendar,* 10-14-08, Yogi Bhajan Lecture, 8-15-96
Page 85, *Aquarian Wisdom Daily Inspirational Calendar,* 11-24-08, Yogi Bhajan Lecture 7-23-87
Page 92, Yogi Bhajan Lecture, 6-16-84
Page 95, Yogi Bhajan Lecture, 4-5-94
Page 108, *Aquarian Wisdom Daily Inspirational Calendar,* 2005
Page 98, *Aquarian Wisdom Daily Inspirational Calendar,* 12-17-97, Yogi Bhajan Lecture, 11-17-08
Page 108, *Aquarian Wisdom Daily Inspirational Calendar,* 2005
Page 110, Yogi Bhajan Lecture, 8-12-90

Page 121, Yogi Bhajan, PhD, *Fountain of Youth,* page 2, Sumpuran Khalsa (3HO Women)

Page 123, Yogi Bhajan Lecture, 1-9-98

Page 133, *Aquarian Wisdom Daily Inspirational Calendar,* 6/15/08, Yogi Bhajan Lecture, 7-22-82

Page 134, Yogi Bhajan Lecture, 2-13-88

Page 147, KRI website Mantra lecture, *Beads of Truth*

Page 148, Yogi Bhajan Lecture, 5-9-83

Page 159, *Aquarian Wisdom Daily Inspirational Calendar,* 2/3/08, Yogi Bhajan, 6-11-95

Page 161, *Aquarian Wisdom Daily Inspirational Calendar,* 10-7-74

Page 171, *Aquarian Wisdom Daily Inspirational Calendar,* 9-13-08, Yogi Bhajan Lecture, 3-27-79

Page 173, *Aquarian Wisdom Daily Inspirational Calendar,* 8-10-06

Page 181, Yogi Bhajan, PhD, *Master's Touch,* page 208, (Kundalini Research Institute, 2000)

Page 182, Yogi Bhajan Lecture, 10-23-79

Page 192, Yogi Bhajan Lecture, 1-1-76

Page 196, Yogi Bhajan, 12-2-99

Page 198, Yogi Bhajan Lecture, 3-6 -80

Page 207, Yogi Bhajan, PhD, page 51, *Praana, Praanee, Praanayam,* (Kundalini Research Institute, 2006)

Page 208, *Aquarian Wisdom Daily Inspirational Calendar,* 7-20-08, Yogi Bhajan Lecture, 3-27-79

Page 219, *Aquarian Wisdom Daily Inspirational Calendar,* 8-11-06

Page 220, Yogi Bhajan Lecture, 4-16-85

Page 229, *Aquarian Wisdom Daily Inspirational Calendar,* 3-3-08, Yogi Bhajan Lecture, 11-24-90

Footnote References

Footnote 1, page 13, Yogi Bhajan Lecture, 5-28-80

Footnote 2, page 44, Yogi Bhajan Lecture, 2-21-80

Footnote 3, page 44, Yogi Bhajan Lecture, 6-16-84

Footnote 4, page 45, Yogi Bhajan Lecture, 6-16-84

Footnote 5, page 46, Yogi Bhajan Lecture, 6-16-84

Footnote 6, page 62, Yogi Bhajan Lecture, 1-9-98

Footnote 7, page 63, Yogi Bhajan Lecture, 1-9-98

Footnote 8, page 71, Yogi Bhajan Lecture, 3-10-80

Footnote 9, page 104, Yogi Bhajan, PhD, *The Aquarian Teacher Textbook,* page 95 (Kundalini Research Institute, 2003)

Footnote 10, page 106, Yogi Bhajan, PhD, *The Aquarian Teacher Textbook,* pages 107, 109, 329 (Kundalini Research Institute, 2003)

Chapter 7: The Ten Bodies In-Depth

SOUL BODY: Yogi Bhajan Lectures: 7-31-81; 9-2-82; 10-9-84; 5-28-80

NEGATIVE, POSITIVE & NEUTRAL MIND: Yogi Bhajan Lectures: 1-9-98; 1-10-98; 1-11-98, 12-3-89; 1-24-86; 3-10-80; 5-9-83; 11-18-89; 10-18-85

PHYSICAL BODY: Yogi Bhajan Lectures: 7-4-00; 10-17-79; 1-24-86; 11-7-77

ARC BODY: Yogi Bhajan Lectures: 3-2-84; 3-6-80; 5-29-93; 7-25-81; 5-20-83; 12-31-84; 11-10-89; 12-31-98

AURIC BODY: Yogi Bhajan Lectures: 2- 21-80; 5-20-83; 5-28-78; 5-20-83

PRANIC BODY: Yogi Bhajan Lectures: 7-5-93;

3-6-80; 11-30-85
SUBTLE BODY: Yogi Bhajan Lectures: 2-21-80; 3-6-80; 5-27-81; 10-06-83; 2-26-89
RADIANT BODY: Yogi Bhajan Lectures: 9-27-88; 3-14-89; 4-25-97; 12-17-97
TEN BODIES: Yogi Bhajan Lecture, 3-27-79

Ten Body Kriyas

Special thanks to Guru Singh Khalsa who meticulously took notes during Yogi Bhajan's Kundalini Yoga classes in Los Angeles from 1969-1972. Yogi Bhajan personally approved write-ups and photographs based on Guru Singh's class notes for the Ten Body kriyas, and Guru Singh was kind enough to give us permission to use his notes to reproduce the kriyas in *Waves of Healing*.

Ten Body Meditations

1. Soul Body: *The Master's Touch,* pg 38, Yogi Bhajan, Ph.D. (Kundalini Research Institute, 2000)
2. Negative Mind: Online at *www.3HO.org/Tantric Numerology*
3. Positive Mind. *KRI Journal of Science & Consciousness,* page 29 (Kundalini Research Institute, 1975)
4. Neutral Mind: *KRI Journal of Science & Consciousness,* page 50 (Kundalini Research Institute, 1975)
5. Physical Body: *The Aquarian Teacher Yoga Manual,* page 137 (Kundalini Research Institute, 2003)

6. Arcline: *The Master's Touch,* page 208 (Kundalini Research Institute, 2000)
7. Aura: Grace of God, *The Aquarian Teacher Yoga Manual,* page 419 (Kundalini Research Institute, 2003)
Kirtan Kriya, *The Aquarian Teacher Yoga Manual,* page 425 (Kundalini Research Institute, 2003)
8. Pranic Body: *The Aquarian Teacher Yoga Manual,* page 401 (Kundalini Research Institute, 2003)
9. Subtle Body: *KRI Journal of Science & Consciousness,* page 63 (Kundalini Research Institute, 1975)
10. Radiant Body: *Sadhana Guidelines,* page 101 (Kundalini Research Institute, 1978)

INDEX

frontal lobe, 196
fulfillment, 40

G

glands, 54, 64, 66, 106, 195
glandular system, 31, 64, 66, 70
God, 17, 18, 28, 29, 37, 38, 58, 62,
70, 72, 77, 78, 85, 92, 93, 94, 95,
96, 133, 190, 192
Golden Cord, 195
grace, 17, 24, 55, 92, 159, 190,
191, 192
gratitude, 77
guidance, 17, 59, 120, 150
Gyan Mudra, 105

H

habits, 29, 30
halo, 13, 55
hapiness, 92
happiness, 50, 51, 71, 79, 93
healer, 17, 18, 39, 90, 95, 231
healing, vi, vii, 13, 26, 28, 29, 32,
33, 39, 52, 79, 85, 90, 91, 95, 161,
162, 192, 231, 232
health, vii, 54, 56, 57, 58, 191, 192
heart, 30, 39, 100, 106, 112, 117,
124, 136, 147, 148, 150, 163, 171,
178, 184, 210, 223
hormones, 63, 64
hypothalamus, 64, 65, 66, 196

I

identity, 22, 24, 29, 44, 56, 58, 64,
71, 93, 95, 104
illness, 23, 28, 29, 30, 31, 33, 40,
50, 57, 79, 85, 90
independence, 32
Infinite, 24, 36, 37, 38, 39, 40, 70,
72, 78, 91, 92, 94, 95, 103, 159,
161, 195, 231
injury, 101
inner voice, 30
innocence, 24
intelligence, 46, 51, 229
intention, 30, 68, 70, 76, 91
intuition, 29, 31, 32, 36, 59, 71

J

Jalandhar Bandh, 106

K

Karam Pad, 90, 91
karma, 38, 70, 95, 180, 181, 229
Kundalini Yoga, iv, 12, 13, 31, 44,
45, 58, 79, 98, 100, 101, 103, 104,
105, 106, 121, 230, 231, 232

L

love, 16, 24, 28, 33, 36, 64, 72, 79,
91, 94, 95, 107, 159, 220
lungs, 45, 57, 103

M

magnetic field, 25, 31, 44, 58, 65,
71, 100, 171
magnetic psyche, 44, 110
mantra, 71, 78, 102, 103, 104, 106,
121, 133, 159, 171, 180, 190, 191,
194, 195, 219, 228, 229
mastery, 40, 54, 133, 159
meditation, 18, 38, 39, 54, 68, 70,
71, 72, 100, 101, 103, 106, 107
menstruation, 101
mind, 12, 13, 17, 18, 22, 29, 30,
31, 32, 36, 38, 44, 45, 46, 50, 51,
52, 53, 54, 57, 59, 60, 62, 63, 64,
65, 66, 71, 84, 85, 93, 100, 103,
104, 105, 122, 123, 124, 133, 134,
136, 146, 147, 148, 150, 158, 159,
171
miracles, 18
Moon, 45, 65
mudra, 105
Mulbandh, 105, 106
music, v, 58, 66, 90, 106, 120, 121,
181

N

Neck Lock, 106
Negative Mind, 12, 51, 52, 53, 62,
122, 123, 124, 132, 133
negativity, 13, 56, 62, 92
nerves, 159, 229
nervous system, 65, 66, 104
neurosis, 36, 93
Neutral Mind, 13, 52, 53, 148,
150, 158
nurturing, 23, 24, 32, 33, 37, 79,
91